Student Note-Taking Guide to Accompany

Concepts of Athletic Training FOURTH EDITION

Ronald P. Pfeiffer
Department of Kinesiology
Boise State University

Brent C. Mangus
Department of Kinesiology
University of Nevada, Las Vegas

Material prepared by
Wendy Schiff
Department of Physical Education
St. Louis Community College-Meramec

JONES AND BARTLETT PUBLISHERS
Sudbury, Massachusetts
BOSTON   TORONTO   LONDON   SINGAPORE

World Headquarters
Jones and Bartlett Publishers
40 Tall Pine Drive
Sudbury, MA 01776
978-443-5000
info@jbpub.com
www.jbpub.com

Jones and Bartlett Publishers Canada
2406 Nikanna Road
Mississauga, ON L5C 2W6
CANADA

Jones and Bartlett Publishers International
Barb House, Barb Mews
London W6 7PA
UK

Cover image © Ryan McVay/Photodisc/Getty Images

Printed in the United States of America
08 07 06 05 04   10 9 8 7 6 5 4 3 2 1

Contents

How This Book Can Help You Learn

All of us have different learning styles. Some of us are visual learners, some more auditory, some learn better by doing an activity. Some students prefer to learn new material using visual aids. Some learn material better when they hear it in a lecture; others learn it better by reading it. Cognitive research has shown that no matter what your learning style, you will learn more if you are actively engaged in the learning process.

The Student Note-Taking Guide will help you learn by providing a structure to your notes and letting you utilize all of the learning styles mentioned above. Students don't need to copy down every word their professor says or recopy their entire textbook. Do the assigned reading, listen in lecture, follow the key points your instructor is making, and write down meaningful notes. After reading and lectures, review your notes and pull out the most important points.

The Student Note-Taking Guide is a great learning tool that follows the chapter topics presented in your textbook, *Concepts of Athletic Training*. The main topics covered in the lectures are listed in the Table of Contents. No more skimming through chapter after chapter trying to find the term you need to understand! If your instructor is using the PowerPoint slides that accompany the text, this guide will save you from having to write down everything that is on the slides. There is space provided for you to jot down the terms and concepts that you feel are most important to each lecture. By working with your Guide, you are seeing, hearing, writing, and, later, reading and reviewing. The more times you are exposed to the material, the better you will learn and understand it. Using different methods of exposure significantly increases your comprehension.

This Guide is the perfect place to write down questions that you want to ask your professor later, interesting ideas that you want to discuss with your study group, or reminders to yourself to go back and study a certain concept again to make sure that you really got it.

Having organized notes is essential at exam time or when doing homework assignments. Your ability to easily locate the important concepts of a recent lecture will help you move along more rapidly, as you don't have to spend time rereading an entire chapter just to reinforce one point that you may not have quite understood.

This Guide is a valuable resource. You've found a wonderful study partner!

Note-Taking Tips

1. It is easier to take notes if you are not hearing the information for the first time. Read the chapter or the material that is about to be discussed before class. This will help you to anticipate what will be said in class, and to have an idea of what to write down. It will also help to read over your notes from the last class. This way you can avoid having to spend the first few minutes of class trying to remember where you left off last time.

2. Don't waste your time trying to write down everything that your professor says. Instead, listen closely and write down only the important points. Review these important points after class to help remind you of related points that were made during the lecture.

3. If the class discussion takes a spontaneous turn, pay attention and participate in the discussion. Only take notes on the conclusions that are relevant to the lecture.

4. Emphasize main points in your notes. You may want to use a highlighter, special notation (asterisks, exclamation points), format (circle, underline), or placement on the page (indented, bulleted). You will find that when you try to recall these points, you will be able to actually picture them on the page.

5. Hearing something repeated, stressed, or summed up can be a signal that it is an important concept to understand.

6. Organize handouts, study guides, and exams in your notebook along with your lecture notes. It may be helpful to use a three-ring binder, so that you can insert pages wherever you need to.

7. When taking notes, you might find it helpful to leave a wide margin on all four sides of the page. Doing this allows you to note names, dates, definitions, etc. for easy access and studying later. It may also be helpful to make notes of questions you want to ask your professor about or research later, ideas or relationships that you want to explore more on your own, or concepts that you don't fully understand.

8. It is best to maintain a separate notebook for each class. Labeling and dating your notes can be helpful when you need to look up information from previous lectures.

9. Make your notes legible, and take notes directly in your notebook. Chances are you won't recopy them no matter how noble your intentions. Spend the time you would have spent recopying the notes studying them instead, drawing conclusions and making connections that you didn't have time for in class.

10. Look over your notes after class while the lecture is still fresh in your mind. Fix illegible items and clarify anything you don't understand. Do this again right before the next class.

Notes

Cauliflower ear - hematoma under skin
  of external ear
- stops blood supply to cartilage
- cartilage dies
- blood products + dead cart. broken up
  + repaired = cauliflower ear
- TREATMENT if swelling + hematoma
  - drain the ear

Concepts of
Athletic Training FOURTH EDITION
Ronald P. Pfeiffer
Brent C. Mangus

Chapter 1

The Concept of Sports Injury

Ronald P. Pfeiffer and Brent C. Mangus
Concepts of Athletic Training FOURTH EDITION

Sports Participation

In the United States, 6.7
million public high school
children are involved in
sports activities annually.

Ronald P. Pfeiffer and Brent C. Mangus
Concepts of Athletic Training FOURTH EDITION

Title IX Education
Assistance Act of 1972

- Since its passing,
  female sports
  participation
  increased by 700%.
- Research indicates
  injuries are sports
  specific, NOT
  gender specific.

Notes

Concepts of Athletic Training
Ronald P. Pfeiffer and Brent C. Mangus

General Injury Data

According to a Pennsylvania study, rates of athletic injuries among of high school students were:

- Football - 46.7%
- Boys' basketball - 10%
- Wrestling - 9.68%
- Girls Basketball - 7.5%

Concepts of Athletic Training
Ronald P. Pfeiffer and Brent C. Mangus

General Injury Data (continued)

In a two-year study of a community sports program, children participating in soccer had the highest rate of injury, followed by baseball, football, and softball.

Contusions were the most common injury.

Concepts of Athletic Training
Ronald P. Pfeiffer and Brent C. Mangus

Definition of Sports Injury

• No universally acceptable definition.

• The majority of today's definitions use "time loss" criteria as the major determinant.

Ronald P. Pfeiffer and Brent C. Mangus
Concepts of Athletic Training FOURTH EDITION

NCAA Definition of Sports Injury

Sports Injury:
- Occurs as a result of participation in organized intercollegiate practice or game.
- Requires medical attention by a team athletic trainer or physician.
- Results in restriction of athlete's participation for one or more days after the injury.

Time lost does not reflect injury's severity.

No standard length of time must be lost to qualify as a specific level of injury severity.

Ronald P. Pfeiffer and Brent C. Mangus
Concepts of Athletic Training FOURTH EDITION

Acute Injuries

Acute Injury - "injury characterized by rapid onset, resulting from a traumatic event"
- Acute injuries typically involve significant trauma followed by pain, swelling, and loss of function.

Critical Force - "magnitude of a single force for which the anatomical structure of interest is damaged"

Ronald P. Pfeiffer and Brent C. Mangus
Concepts of Athletic Training FOURTH EDITION

Chronic Injuries

Chronic Injury - "injury characterized by a slow, insidious onset, implying a gradual development of structural damage"
- Chronic injuries develop over time and are often associated with repetitive, cyclic activities, such as running.
- These injuries are commonly called "overuse injuries." Common sites include the Achilles tendon, patellar tendon, and the rotator cuff.

Ronald P. Pfeiffer and Brent C. Mangus
Concepts of Athletic Training FOURTH EDITION

Soft Tissues

Soft Tissues
  Muscles
  Fascia
  Tendons
  Joint capsules
  Ligaments
  Blood vessels
  Nerves

Ronald P. Pfeiffer and Brent C. Mangus
Concepts of Athletic Training FOURTH EDITION

Catastrophic Injury

Catastrophic Injuries:

• Involve damage to the brain and/or spinal cord.

• Can be life threatening or permanent.

• Can occur as a direct or indirect result of sports participation.

Ronald P. Pfeiffer and Brent C. Mangus
Concepts of Athletic Training FOURTH EDITION

Connective Tissue Injuries

Sprains are injuries to ligaments.

• First-degree: mild with no swelling
• Second-degree: ligament damage, pain, and dysfunction
• Third-degree: complete tear of ligament(s)

Notes

Types of fractures
- greenstick
- transverse
- comminuted
-

Concepts of Athletic Training FOURTH EDITION

Connective Tissue Injuries

Strains are injuries to tendon, muscle, or musculotendinous junction.

- First-degree strain: mild with no swelling, pain noticeable with use
- Second-degree strain: more extensive soft-tissue damage, pain, and moderate loss of function
- Third-degree strain: complete rupture, significant swelling & loss of function

---

Concepts of Athletic Training FOURTH EDITION

Connective Tissue Injuries

Contusions are commonly referred to as "bruises."

- Contusions are associated with pain, stiffness, swelling, ecchymosis, and hematoma.

- May result in **myositis ossificans**.

Concepts of Athletic Training FOURTH EDITION

Skeletal Tissue Injuries

Fractures are breaks or cracks in a bone.

Types of Fractures
- Closed
- Open
- Stress
- Salter-Harris

Ronald P. Pfeiffer and Brent C. Mangus
Concepts of Athletic Training FOURTH EDITION

Dislocations

Dislocation- "displacement of contiguous surfaces or bones comprising a joint"

Subluxation: partial displacement

Luxation: total displacement

All dislocations should be diagnosed and treated by a physician. *Severe sprain*

Ronald P. Pfeiffer and Brent C. Mangus
Concepts of Athletic Training FOURTH EDITION

Injury Recognition

Coach's role:

- Treat any suspected injury as an actual injury until proven otherwise.
- Recognize and discriminate injuries that require medical referral from those that do not require such attention.

Schools or sponsoring agency should make every effort to hire an NATABOC-Certified Athletic Trainer.

Ronald P. Pfeiffer and Brent C. Mangus
Concepts of Athletic Training FOURTH EDITION

Epidemiology of Sports Injury

- Epidemiology - "study of the distribution of diseases, injuries, or other health states in human populations for the purpose of identifying and implementing measures to prevent their development and spread"

- Scientific studies of sports injuries are a relatively recent trend.

result... no spearing

_____
_____
_____
_____
_____
_____
_____
_____
_____
_____
_____
_____
_____
_____
_____
_____
_____
_____
_____
_____
_____
_____
_____
_____
_____
_____
_____
_____
_____
_____
_____
_____
_____
_____
_____

Ronald P. Pfeiffer and Brent C. Mangus
Concepts of Athletic Training FOURTH EDITION

Epidemiology of Sports Injuries

Sports injury epidemiology involves determining risk factors that play a causative role in the injury.

- Hypotheses are developed to test for statistical relationships between risk factors and injury.

Ronald P. Pfeiffer and Brent C. Mangus
Concepts of Athletic Training FOURTH EDITION

Classification of Sports

[handwritten: on exam (see book)]

American Academy of Pediatrics has developed categories of sports.

- Contact/collision
- Limited contact/impact
- Non-contact

Ronald P. Pfeiffer and Brent C. Mangus
Concepts of Athletic Training FOURTH EDITION

Extent of Injuries: Tackle Football

- 34% of players injured; offensive players have higher risk than defensive players.
- Hip, thigh, and leg regions injured most often.
- 2.4% of injuries required surgery, and of those 59.4% involved the knee.

Notes

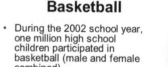

Extent of Injuries: Tackle Football

- Contusions, strains, sprains, and fractures are common injuries.

- Older players have higher risk than younger ones.

- Spinal cord and brain injuries are a major concern.

Extent of Injuries: Basketball

- During the 2002 school year, one million high school children participated in basketball (male and female combined).
- Players have a high risk for lower extremity injuries.
- Ankle sprains are the most common injury.
- Girls have higher risk of knee injuries than boys and are more likely to require surgery.

Extent of Injuries: Baseball

In 2002, over 450,000 high school boys participated.

Nearly 12% sustained injuries.
Forearm/wrist/hand or shoulder/arm were often injured.

Of these injuries, most were strains or sprains.

Concepts of Athletic Training FOURTH EDITION
Ronald P. Pfeiffer and Brent C. Mangus

Extent of Injuries: Baseball

- Children between the ages 5 and 14 have increased vulnerability to chest impact injuries from balls.
- Eye injuries from pitched balls are a concern.
- Chronic elbow injuries are a concern for adolescent pitchers.
  - Sidearm pitching presents the greatest risk for elbow problems.

Concepts of Athletic Training FOURTH EDITION
Ronald P. Pfeiffer and Brent C. Mangus

Extent of Injuries: Wrestling

- In 2002, there were over 240,000 high school participants.
  - About 27% sustained injuries.
- Collisions with opponents and mats, and takedown and escape maneuvers resulted in various injuries.
- Shoulder/arm, knee, and forearm/wrist/hand were injured most often.
  - Most of these injuries were strains & sprains.
- Friction burns, skin infections, and "cauliflower ear" are also common injuries.

Concepts of Athletic Training FOURTH EDITION
Ronald P. Pfeiffer and Brent C. Mangus

Extent of Injuries: Volleyball

- During 2002, nearly 400,000 high school girls participated.
- Nearly 15% were injured, most of these injuries were sprains.
- Ankle/foot region is most often injured.

Notes

_____

_____

_____

_____

_____

_____

_____

_____

_____

_____

_____

_____

_____

_____

_____

_____

_____

_____

_____

_____

_____

_____

Ronald P. Pfeiffer and Brent C. Mangus
Concepts of Athletic Training FOURTH EDITION

Extent of Injuries: Soccer

In the United States, there are 12 million participants under 18 years of age.

During the 2002 season almost:

- 340,000 high school boys participated.
- 300,000 high school girls participated.

Ronald P. Pfeiffer and Brent C. Mangus
Concepts of Athletic Training FOURTH EDITION

Extent of Injuries: Soccer (continued)

Contusions are the most common injury, with the knee, ankle, and shin most often injured.

- Heading may result in injury, but no reliable research to confirm this hypothesis.

- Improperly constructed, movable soccer goals have been involved in a number of severe injuries and deaths.

Q's

No % of injuries

No #1, 2, 3, 4, 11, 12, 14, 15   Yes   13

chronic   cut   trac   epi
acute   sp   st lux

Chapter 2: The Athletic Health Care Team

Notes

_____

_____

_____

_____

_____

_____

_____

_____

_____

_____

_____

_____

_____

_____

_____

_____

_____

_____

_____

_____

_____

_____

_____

_____

_____

_____

_____

_____

_____

_____

_____

_____

_____

_____

_____

_____

_____

_____

_____

_____

_____

Concepts of Athletic Training FOURTH EDITION

Ronald P. Pfeiffer
Brent C. Mangus

Chapter 2

The Athletic Health Care Team

Ronald P. Pfeiffer and Brent C. Mangus
Concepts of Athletic Training FOURTH EDITION

Sports Medicine

Definition: "A field that uses a holistic, comprehensive, and multidisciplinary approach to health care for those engaged in sporting or recreational activity.

Practitioners include primary care physicians, orthopedic surgeons, athletic trainers, sports physical therapists, dentists, exercise physiologists, conditioning coaches, and sports nutritionists.

Ronald P. Pfeiffer and Brent C. Mangus
Concepts of Athletic Training FOURTH EDITION

Key Team Members

Coaches

Team Physicians

NATABOC-Certified Athletic Trainer

Notes

_____

_____

_____

_____

_____

_____

_____

_____

_____

_____

_____

_____

_____

_____

_____

_____

_____

_____

_____

_____

_____

_____

_____

_____

_____

_____

_____

_____

_____

_____

_____

_____

_____

_____

_____

_____

_____

_____

_____

_____

_____

_____

_____

Ronald P. Pfeiffer and Brent C. Mangus
Concepts of Athletic Training FOURTH EDITION

Coaches

Coaches in public school settings should be trained in:

Basic conditioning procedures.
Maintenance and fitting of protective equipment.
First aid and CPR.
Operation of an automatic external defibrillator.
Recognition and management of common sports injuries.
Skills instruction.

Ronald P. Pfeiffer and Brent C. Mangus
Concepts of Athletic Training FOURTH EDITION

Team Physician

Team physician's role in medical management of athletes includes:

- Coordinating preparticipation screening, examination, and evaluation.
- Managing injuries on the field.
- Providing medical management of injuries and illnesses.
- Coordinating rehab and return to participation.
- Providing for proper preparation for safe return to participation after illness or injury.
- Integrating expertise with other health care providers.
- Providing education and counseling.
- Providing proper documentation and medical record keeping.

Ronald P. Pfeiffer and Brent C. Mangus
Concepts of Athletic Training FOURTH EDITION

Athletic Trainer

NATABOC-certified athletic trainer: an allied health care professional (baccalaureate or masters degree) with extensive education in clinical care & prevention of sports injuries.

Athletic trainers receive formal instruction in:
- Injury prevention.
- Recognition, evaluation and immediate care.
- Rehabilitation and reconditioning.
- Health care organization and administration.
- Professional development and responsibility.

Concepts of Athletic Training
Ronald P. Pfeiffer and Brent C. Mangus

NATABOC Certification

To qualify:

- Complete a CAAHEP-accredited educational program.

- Take certification examination that is offered 5 times/year.

Concepts of Athletic Training
Ronald P. Pfeiffer and Brent C. Mangus

Professional Settings for Athletic Trainers

- Public school teacher/athletic trainer
- Professional team's athletic trainer
- Corporate on-site athletic trainer
- Athletic trainer for a sports medicine clinic or hospital

Q's

No 1, 2, 3, 5, 6, 7, 8, 9, 10   Yes 4,

Cert. Stuff

Notes

Concepts of
Athletic Training FOURTH EDITION
Ronald P. Pfeiffer
Brent C. Mangus

Chapter 3

The Law of Sports Injury

Ronald P. Pfeiffer and Brent C. Mangus
Concepts of Athletic Training FOURTH EDITION

The Coach

- The coach is typically the first person at the scene of an injury.
- The coach's decisions and actions are critical.
- Inappropriate decisions may jeopardize the athlete's health and result in legal action.
- A recent study of high school coaches found:
  - A significant percentage of coaches lacked adequate first aid knowledge.
  - When losing a close game, conflict of interest arose when a starting player was injured.

Ronald P. Pfeiffer and Brent C. Mangus
Concepts of Athletic Training FOURTH EDITION

Concept of Tort

- **Tort**: "harm, other than a breach of contract, done to another for which the law holds the wrongdoer responsible"
- **Negligence**: "the failure to do what a reasonably careful and prudent person would have done under the same or like circumstances, or doing of something that a reasonably careful and prudent person would not have done under the same or like circumstances"

Notes

Ronald P. Pfeiffer and Brent C. Mangus

Concepts of Athletic Training FOURTH EDITION

Negligence

Act of commission -- acting in an improper way

Act of omission -- failure to act

Elements for proof of negligence include:
- Duty.
- A breach of duty.
- Proximate or legal cause.
- Damage.

Ronald P. Pfeiffer and Brent C. Mangus

Concepts of Athletic Training FOURTH EDITION

Other Terms Relating to Tort Cases

- Contributory negligence
- Comparative negligence
- Assumption of risk
- Act of God (act of nature)

Ronald P. Pfeiffer and Brent C. Mangus

Concepts of Athletic Training FOURTH EDITION

What Is Your Liability?

Doctrine of sovereign immunity does not guarantee immunity for coaches.

- Coach must use reasonable care to avoid creating foreseeable risk of harm.

- Coach should have a legal contract that outlines specific coaching duties.

Concepts of Athletic Training FOURTH EDITION
Ronald P. Pfeiffer and Brent C. Mangus

What Is Your Liability?

Potential liabilities for coaches include:

- Failure to provide competent personnel, instruction, and proper equipment.
- Failure to warn or supervise.
- Failure to treat an injured athlete properly.
- Failure to ensure that an athlete is ready to participate.

Concepts of Athletic Training FOURTH EDITION
Ronald P. Pfeiffer and Brent C. Mangus

Are You Protected?

- Coaches need to be vigilant regarding risks to athletes.
- Coaches should acquire liability insurance.
- Contact employer to determine if liability protection is provided.

Concepts of Athletic Training FOURTH EDITION
Ronald P. Pfeiffer and Brent C. Mangus

To Reduce Your Chances of Going to Court

To reduce your chances of going to court, have:

- A written contract.
- First aid/CPR training.
- An emergency plan.
- Parental consent forms for those under 18 years of age.
- Documentation of all injuries.
- PPEs.
- In-service seminars.
- Inspections of facilities/equipment.
- Effective lines of communication.

Notes

Ronald P. Pfeiffer and Brent C. Mangus

Concepts of Athletic Training FOURTH EDITION

If You Get Sued

- Call your insurance company and your lawyer.
- Write a detailed description of events related to the incident & obtain signed statements from witnesses.
- Make NO statement to the media or other parties without getting legal counsel.

No

Yes 1, 2, 3, 4, 5, 6, 7, 8, 11

Chapter 4: Sports-Injury Prevention

Notes

Concepts of
Athletic Training FOURTH EDITION
Ronald P. Pfeiffer
Brent C. Mangus

Chapter 4

Sports-Injury Prevention

Ronald P. Pfeiffer and Brent C. Mangus
Concepts of Athletic Training FOURTH EDITION

Causative Factors in Injury

Intrinsic factors
   Age
   Gender
   Body size
   Injury history
   Fitness level
   Muscle strength
   Skill level
   Psychological state

Ronald P. Pfeiffer and Brent C. Mangus
Concepts of Athletic Training FOURTH EDITION

Causative Factors in Injury

Extrinsic factors

Equipment
Environment
Type of activity
Conditioning errors

Intervention Strategies

- Extrinsic factors such as faulty equipment, dangerous facilities, etc. can be easily recognized.

- Athletes in high-risk sports MUST be educated about hazards and prevention.

- NCAA and NFSH have developed guidelines for medical evaluation of student/athletes.

Ronald P. Pfeiffer and Brent C. Mangus
Concepts of Athletic Training FOURTH EDITION

Intervention

NCAA Guideline 1B

- PPE (pre-participation physical examination) is required upon entrance into athletic program; thereafter, only updated medical history unless additional medical exam is warranted based on this history.

NFSH policy

- PPE required prior to first year of participation.

The primary purpose of PPE: Identify preexisting injury risk factors as well as ascertain any injuries/diseases that are potentially problematic.

Ronald P. Pfeiffer and Brent C. Mangus
Concepts of Athletic Training FOURTH EDITION

PPEs

Historically known as "annual physical," "physical exam," and "preparticipation medical evaluation."

- Primary purpose is to identify pre-existing injury risk factors/diseases.

- Physical exams can identify spina bifida occulta, absence of one of paired organs, postural problems, high blood pressure, cardiac defects, allergies, and skin infections.

Notes

PPEs

AAP recommends PPE biannually with interim "history" prior to a new season.

Two forms of PPEs:

- Office-based works well when physician is familiar with athlete's medical history
- Station-based screening is useful for examining many athletes.

All information obtained during examination should be handled to protect athlete's confidentiality.

Preseason Conditioning

General Conditioning: aerobic fitness, muscular strength and endurance, flexibility, nutrition, and body composition

Sports-Specific Conditioning: all aspects of the sport that are unique to it

Conditioning

Aerobic fitness

- Regardless of sport, all athletes benefit from improving aerobic fitness.

Muscular strength & endurance:

- increased connective tissue strength
- increased bone density
- improved strength ratios
- increased muscular endurance

Conditioning

Flexibility: "ROM in a given joint or combination of joints"

- Determinants include tissue temperature, bone structure, tissue mass, age, and gender.
- Two types of flexibility are static & dynamic flexibility.
- Four types of stretching are ballistic, static, PNF, and passive.

Conditioning

Nutrition & body composition:

- The body can respond more effectively when it receives proper nourishment.
- Coaches, parents, and athletes must take care to avoid an overemphasis on leanness.

Muscle Strength, Power, Endurance

- Periodization: process of arranging training around specific goals and objectives.
  - Organizes training into cyclic structure
  - Manipulates exercise frequency, intensity, and duration
  - Helps prevent training-induced injury

Notes

Preseason Conditioning

- Most training programs designed around 1 year period of time.
  - macrocycle
  - microcycle – 2 to 4 weeks
  - mesocycle – several successive microcycles
  - transition phase – 2 to 4 weeks between training seasons or microcycles

Modification of Extrinsic Risk Factors

- Practice/competition environmental conditions, especially heat & humidity, must be assessed.

- Facilities must be designed, maintained, and frequently inspected for safety.

Coaching personnel and administrators MUST monitor these factors.

Modification of Intrinsic Risk Factors

Many intrinsic factors can be modified with a conditioning program.

General & sports specific conditioning

- General conditioning focuses on aerobic fitness, muscle strength, muscle endurance, flexibility, body composition, etc.
- Sports-specific conditioning focuses on all aspects of the particular sport that are unique.

_____

_____

_____

_____

_____

_____

_____

_____

_____

_____

Ronald P. Pfeiffer and Brent C. Mangus
Concepts of Athletic Training FOURTH EDITION

Modification of Extrinsic Factors

- Indoor facilities: lighting, playing surfaces, room dimensions
- Protective equipment: helmets, shoulder pads, etc.
- External facilities: safety fences, batting cages, location of dugouts, soccer goal construction, water and sanitation facilities, and EMS access routes

Q's

No periodization detail........

Yes 1, 2, 5, 6, 8, 9, 10,

Notes

Concepts of Athletic Training FOURTH EDITION
Ronald P. Pfeiffer
Brent C. Mangus

Chapter 5

The Psychology of Injury

Ronald P. Pfeiffer and Brent C. Mangus
Concepts of Athletic Training FOURTH EDITION

Personality Variables

Personality is defined as "...stable enduring qualities of the individual."

Characteristics that are related to sports injuries include:
- General personality.
- Trait anxiety.
- Locus of control.
- Self-concept.

Ronald P. Pfeiffer and Brent C. Mangus
Concepts of Athletic Training FOURTH EDITION

Psychosocial Variables and Injury

- Psychosocial variables develop through interaction between person and environment.
- Stressful life events can be positive or negative episodes.
- A strong relationship exists between negative events and sports injury.
- Athletes with high degrees of coping ability are less likely to get injured.

Notes

_____
_____
_____
_____
_____
_____
_____
_____
_____
_____
_____
_____
_____
_____
_____
_____
_____
_____
_____
_____
_____
_____
_____
_____
_____
_____
_____
_____
_____
_____
_____
_____
_____
_____
_____
_____

Competitive Stress and Adolescents

As more children participate in sports, there are more concerns regarding the psychological effects.

- Intensity of competition has increased.
- Pressure to win is a concern.
- Young athletes may be more prone to injury, psychosomatic illness, burnout, and other stress related problems.
- Coaches and parents must take care to avoid forcing children beyond their ability to cope.

Psychophysiological Responses

Injury is a psychological stressor **for athletes.**

According to Weiss & Troxel:

- **Phase one –The athlete adapts to activity restriction.**
- **Phase two – The athlete appraises short- and long-term significance of the injury.**
- **Phase three – The athlete experiences emotional responses.**
- **Final stage– The athlete deals with long-term consequences.**

Psychology of the Injured Athlete

Recommendations involve:

- Treating the person, not just the injury.
- Treating the person as an individual.
- Keeping in mind the importance of communication skills.
- Remembering the relationship between physical & psychological skills.
- Seeking the help of a sports psychologist.

Concepts of Athletic Training

Eating Disorders

Majority of sports have narrow parameters for appropriate body type.

- Some sports demand leanness for success.
- Media exposure focuses on physical appearance, especially for females.
- Emphasis on the ideal body has negative effects.

Concepts of Athletic Training

Eating Disorders (continued)

Anorexia nervosa – self-starvation motivated by obsession with thinness and overwhelming fear of fat

Bulimia nervosa - repeated bouts of binge eating followed by purging

Concepts of Athletic Training

Eating Disorders (continued)

- Female athletes are more likely to practice pathogenic dietary habits than males.
- Rosen et al., found that 32% of athletes practiced some form of pathogenic eating behavior.
- Little is known about pathogenic eating disorders in male athletes, for example, "making weight" in wrestling.

Sport Specificity and Eating Disorders

- There is a higher incidence of eating disorders in gymnastics, distance running, diving, and figure skating.
- In a gymnastics study (n=215), over 60% reported disordered eating behaviors.

Notes

Concepts of Athletic Training FOURTH EDITION
Ronald P. Pfeiffer and Brent C. Mangus

Eating Disorders (continued)

Eating disorders are becoming problems in sports such as field hockey, softball, volleyball, track, and tennis.

Associated physical problems include esophageal inflammation, erosion of tooth enamel, hormone imbalances, and amenorrhea.

Depression and anxiety often affect people with eating disorders.

Concepts of Athletic Training FOURTH EDITION
Ronald P. Pfeiffer and Brent C. Mangus

Eating Disorders (continued)

Prevention efforts include:

- Placing less emphasis on weight.
- Avoiding referral to weight in a negative manner.
- Avoiding mandatory weigh-ins.
- Avoiding ostracizing athlete for being overweight.

Coaches and parents need to be alert for early warning signs.

Concepts of Athletic Training FOURTH EDITION
Ronald P. Pfeiffer and Brent C. Mangus

Eating Disorders (continued)

Treatment:

- Ranges from counseling to hospitalization.
- May include psychological counseling as eating disorders can be symptoms of severe psychological problems such as depression.

One-third of all cases do not respond to therapy.

No   Yes 1, 2, 3, 6, 7, 11

Notes

Concepts of
Athletic Training FOURTH EDITION
Ronald P. Pfeiffer
Brent C. Mangus

Chapter 6

Nutritional Considerations

Ronald P. Pfeiffer and Brent C. Mangus
Concepts of Athletic Training FOURTH EDITION

Background Information

Diet influences every aspect of sports participation.

- Certified athletic trainers are most knowledgeable about nutrition.

Not always true

- Coaches and athletes often lack reliable nutrition information and incorporate unfounded nutritional practices into training programs.

---

9 kilocalories for fat
4 kilocalories for protein

Ronald P. Pfeiffer and Brent C. Mangus
Concepts of Athletic Training FOURTH EDITION

Nutrient Overview

Carbohydrates (CHO) provide energy for high-intensity exercise.

- Experts recommend 60% to 70% of calories be supplied by CHO.
- Each gram provides 4 kilocalories.
- Glycogen is the body's storage form of CHO.
- Carbohydrate (glycogen) loading can benefit athletes involved in aerobic sports, especially activities lasting 60 minutes or more.

Notes

_____

_____

_____

_____

_____

_____

_____

_____

_____

_____

_____

Proteins:
  provides energy for anorexics

_____

_____

_____

_____

_____

_____

_____

_____

_____

_____

_____

_____

_____

_____

_____

_____

_____

Ronald P. Pfeiffer and Brent C. Mangus
Concepts of Athletic Training FOURTH EDITION

Nutrient Overview (continued)

Fats (lipids) are needed for energy, insulation, and protection of organs.

- Fatty acids and glycerol make up simple fats. Fatty acids can be saturated or unsaturated.
- Experts recommendation that fats comprise 30% or less of total calories.
- Each gram of fat supplies 9 kilocalories.

Ronald P. Pfeiffer and Brent C. Mangus
Concepts of Athletic Training FOURTH EDITION

Nutrient Overview (continued)

Proteins are comprised of amino acids; 20 different amino acids are used to make thousands of proteins.

- Muscle protein is an energy source for muscles during prolonged exercise (up to 10% to 15% of energy needs).
- There are 9 *essential* amino acids.

Ronald P. Pfeiffer and Brent C. Mangus
Concepts of Athletic Training FOURTH EDITION

Nutrient Overview (continued)

Protein supplementation is not recommended because the excess can:
- Increase saturated fat in the diet.
- Overtax the liver and kidneys.
- No scientific evidence that protein supplements enhance muscles.
- During intense training, 1.2 to 1.8 grams of protein/kg body weight are recommended.

Best way to obtain protein is by eating food.

Notes

_____
_____
_____
_____
_____
_____
_____
_____
_____
_____
_____
_____
_____
_____
_____
_____
_____
_____
_____
_____
_____
_____
_____
_____
_____
_____
_____
_____
_____
_____
_____
_____
_____
_____

Ronald P. Pfeiffer and Brent C. Mangus
Concepts of Athletic Training FOURTH EDITION
Nutrient Overview (continued)

Vitamins have various functions; they generally help regulate metabolism and tissue generation.

- Some vitamins are antioxidants that protect against free radicals.
- Vitamins provide no calories.
- There are water- and fat-soluble types of vitamins. Fat-soluble vitamins are more likely to cause toxicity.
- A balanced diet supplies vitamins; a multiple vitamin supplement may be necessary.

Ronald P. Pfeiffer and Brent C. Mangus
Concepts of Athletic Training FOURTH EDITION
Nutrient Overview (continued)

Minerals are elements needed for various body functions.

- Calcium is most prevalent mineral in body.
- There is no scientific evidence to support taking excess minerals for performance.
- Taking a multiple vitamin/mineral supplement is OK.
- _Megadoses_ should be avoided.
- Females may be at risk of calcium deficiency and osteoporosis.

Ronald P. Pfeiffer and Brent C. Mangus
Concepts of Athletic Training FOURTH EDITION
Nutrient Overview (continued)

Water is necessary for body functions, including heat regulation and waste elimination.

- Adult water requirement is approx. 2.5 liters daily, but it can increase to 5 to 10 liters due to heavy exercise and environmental conditions.
- Water lost during exercise needs to be replaced to maintain body's fluid balance.

Ronald P. Pfeiffer and Brent C. Mangus
Concepts of Athletic Training FOURTH EDITION

Dietary Habits of Athletes

- Eck's study of 43 university football players indicated their diets were 34.7% CHO, 17% protein, and 42% fat.
- Recommended proportions are 45% to 70% CHO, 12% to 15% protein, and 20% fat.
- Myths such as high protein requirement persist.

Ronald P. Pfeiffer and Brent C. Mangus
Concepts of Athletic Training FOURTH EDITION

Dietary Habits of Athletes

Conclusions:

- Many athletes do not consume proper proportions of protein, CHO, and fat.
- Adolescent athletes need as much as 1.5 to 2 grams of protein/kg body weight daily.
- Many tackle football players consume excess protein and fat.
- Athletes in sports that require lean bodies tend to eat diets with insufficient calories.
- Athletes eat too much "junk food."
- Most athletes' diets are low in calcium, iron, & zinc.

Ronald P. Pfeiffer and Brent C. Mangus
Concepts of Athletic Training FOURTH EDITION

Diet and Wrestling

Wrestlers often follow unhealthy weight loss procedures to compete in lighter category.

- Rapid weight loss occurs via dehydration.
- Water weighs 7 lbs/gallon.
- Dehydration occurs by use of laxatives and diuretics, fluid restriction, induced sweating, and starvation.

Notes

Diet and Wrestling (continued)

Short-term effects of repeated bouts of extreme weight loss include:

- Increased blood viscosity.
- Blood clots.
- Kidney and liver problems.
- Ulcers.

Long-term effects include interfering with normal growth.

Wrestling Minimum Weight Project (WMWP)

Wisconsin instituted WMWP in 1989.

- Weight loss must be no more than 3 lbs. of weight loss/week.
- A minimum 7% body fat level was established.
- Testing of athletes, along with nutrition education for coaches, was done by trained volunteers.

WMWP (continued)

The NFSH has modified its wrestling rule #1-3-1 to state: "The recommended minimum body fat should not be lower than 7%."

Notes

Ronald P. Pfeiffer and Brent C. Mangus
Concepts of Athletic Training FOURTH EDITION

What Can the Coach Do?

Coaches are a source of nutrition information.

- People planning to enter the coaching profession should take at least one basic college nutrition course.
- Attend in-service meetings, professional conferences, or community education programs in sports nutrition.
- Subscribe to professional journals that include nutrition articles.

Ronald P. Pfeiffer and Brent C. Mangus
Concepts of Athletic Training FOURTH EDITION

What Can the Coach Do? (continued)

- Locate nutrition experts, including dietitians, and university nutrition or sports medicine faculty.
- Have athletes keep a record of their diet that is reviewed periodically by a person knowledgeable in nutrition.
- When working with children, discuss nutritional needs of the athlete with parents.

Ronald P. Pfeiffer and Brent C. Mangus
Concepts of Athletic Training FOURTH EDITION

General Dietary Guidelines for Athletes

Three Goals

- Nutritional maintenance and development during training
- Pre-competition preparation
- Nutrition during competition

Notes

Nutrition During Training

Recommendations include:

- 10% to 15% of calories from protein, 30% from fat, and the remainder from CHO.
- 1.5 to 2.0 grams of protein/kg of body weight/day.
- Little need for vitamin/mineral supplements if diet is well-balanced.
- Using simple terms when educating young athletes about nutrition.

USDA Food Guide

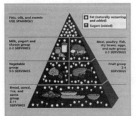

Nutritional information
Food Guide Pyramid

Pre-competition Diets

- Avoid eating meals 2 to 3 hours before event.
- Eat low-fat, easy to digest foods 3 to 4 hours before competition.
- Liquid meals contribute to hydration and are less likely to cause bloating or "heavy" feeling than solid meals.
- Foods should provide 150 to 300 grams of CHO or 3 to 5 grams/kg of body weight.

Concepts of Athletic Training
Ronald P. Pfeiffer and Brent C. Mangus

Nutrition During Competition

- During long-duration exercise (1 to 3 hours at 70% to 80% VO_{2max}), CHO consumption helps muscle cells rely on blood glucose for energy.

- Recommended source of CHO is 8 oz. of a 5% CHO solution consumed every 15 min.

Concepts of Athletic Training
Ronald P. Pfeiffer and Brent C. Mangus

Weight vs. Fat Management

- Body weight consists of water, fat, and lean tissue.
- When athlete fails to consume enough calories to meet needs, fat is metabolized for energy.
- Per unit volume, muscle is denser than fat.
- Fasting results in protein breakdown.
- In many cases, frequent weighing has limited value.

Concepts of Athletic Training
Ronald P. Pfeiffer and Brent C. Mangus

Minimal Competitive Weight

- Athletes should weigh themselves once/week at the same time of day and after going to the bathroom.
- Males should have at least 5% of their total body composition in the form of fat.
- Females should have at least 8 to 10% of their total body composition as fat.

Concepts of Athletic Training

Ronald P. Pfeiffer and Brent C. Mangus

Minimal Competitive Weight (MCW)

Sample Male Equation:

A 135 lb male with 14% body fat has LBW = 135 x .14 = 18.9 lb fat

135 lb - 18.9 (fat weight) = 116.10 lb (LBW)

MCW = 116.10/0.95 = 122.21 lb

Concepts of Athletic Training

Ronald P. Pfeiffer and Brent C. Mangus

Minimal Competitive Weight (MCW)

Sample Female Equation:

115 lb female athlete with 12% body fat has a LBW = 135 x .12 = 13.8 lb of fat

115 lb - 13.8 lb (fat weight) = 101.20 lb (LBW)

MCW = 101.20/0.92 = 110.00 lb

Concepts of Athletic Training

Ronald P. Pfeiffer and Brent C. Mangus

Nutrition and Injury Recovery

Weight gain can occur with forced inactivity.

- Recommend alternative physical activity during recovery.
  - Runners can ride stationary bikes or use running in swimming pools.
- Athletes who are ill/injured should reduce total caloric intake until healthy to avoid excess weight gain.

Notes

Supplements and Ergogenic Aids

Ephedra
Testosterone precursors
Creatine
Amino acids and HMB
Herbals
Anabolic steroids
Erythropoietin
Stimulants
GHB

Keep a good 3 day dietary log
(1 day on Weekend)

Q No 2, 3,   Yes 1, 4, 6, 8, 13, 14

Quiz on Mon

Notes

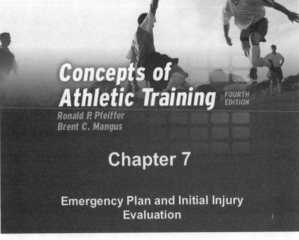

Concepts of Athletic Training FOURTH EDITION
Ronald P. Pfeiffer
Brent C. Mangus

Chapter 7

Emergency Plan and Initial Injury
Evaluation

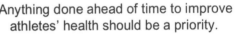

Ronald P. Pfeiffer and Brent C. Mangus
Concepts of Athletic Training FOURTH EDITION

Emergency Plan

Anything done ahead of time to improve
athletes' health should be a priority.

Failure to have an emergency plan is
grounds for negligence.

Ronald P. Pfeiffer and Brent C. Mangus
Concepts of Athletic Training FOURTH EDITION

Emergency Plan Features

The emergency plan:

- Identifies personnel directly involved in carrying
  out the plan.
- Specifies necessary equipment.
- Establishes a mechanism for communication.
- Is derived from overall emergency planning
  policies.
- Incorporates local emergency care facilities.

Concepts of Athletic Training FOURTH EDITION

Ronald P. Pfeiffer and Brent C. Mangus

Emergency Plan Features (continued)

The emergency plan:

– Specifies documentation needed to support plan implementation and evaluation.

– Is reviewed and rehearsed at least annually, and the results of these efforts are documented.

– Is reviewed by the administration and legal counsel of the sponsoring organization or institution.

Concepts of Athletic Training FOURTH EDITION

Ronald P. Pfeiffer and Brent C. Mangus

The Emergency Team

Members of the emergency team are personnel directly involved in interscholastic sports programming (high school level), including:

- **Coaches.**
- **Administrators.**
- **Team physician.**
- **Athletic trainer.**
- **Local EMS staff.**

Concepts of Athletic Training FOURTH EDITION

Ronald P. Pfeiffer and Brent C. Mangus

Functions of Emergency Team Members

Members of the emergency care team are responsible for:

- Immediate care of athlete.
- Emergency equipment retrieval.
- Activation of EMS, if necessary.
- Directing EMS to injury scene.

P. 85

Emergency Plan

Plan should be comprehensive and include:

- Procedures for both home and away events.
- Steps for dealing with emergency situations affecting athletes, fans, and sideline participants.
- Locations of phones (coaches should have cell phones).
- Emergency phone numbers.
- Directions to the site.
- Access points.

First Aid Training

- **All personnel** should be trained in basic first aid, CPR, and use of AEDs.
- Training should be conducted by nationally recognized organizations, e.g., the American Heart Association.
- Personnel should upgrade training at least every 3 years.
- Personnel should have periodic "mock" emergency drills to rehearse the plan.

Injury-Evaluation Procedures

Coach's responsibility is the immediate care of acute injury – this is critical.

- Coach should maintain a "clear head" and remain objective.
- Coach must indicate that he or she is in charge.
- By law, coaches are most often held accountable for proper care when no physician or athletic trainer is present.

Notes

Injury-Evaluation Procedures

Coaching personnel should have **BLS** training that focuses on life-threatening situations.

Primary BLS skills are:
- Airway assessment and opening techniques.
- Rescue breathing.
- CPR.

Coaches **must** distinguish minor from major injuries.

Initial Survey: Nervous System

Is the athlete responsive?

- Note if the athlete is alert. Are the athlete's eyes open? Can the athlete state name, date, time, and location?
- If the athlete does not appear to be alert, establish verbal communication.
- If the athlete is unable to communicate, verify response to painful stimulus.

Initial Survey: Nervous System (continued)

Is the athlete responsive?

- If athlete fails to show any response, he or she is "unresponsive to any stimulus."

If spinal or head injury is suspected, immobilize head and neck **immediately**.

Notes

___

Concepts of Athletic Training FOURTH EDITION
Ronald P. Pfeiffer and Brent C. Mangus

Initial Survey: Airway Assessment

Ask athlete a simple question.

- A response indicates the airway is open and circulation is adequate.
- If athlete is unresponsive and has no apparent serious head or spinal injuries:
  - Use head-tilt/chin lift method (do not remove helmet or face mask).

Concepts of Athletic Training FOURTH EDITION
Ronald P. Pfeiffer and Brent C. Mangus

Initial Survey: Airway Assessment (continued)

If the person is not breathing and spinal or head injury is suspected:

Use jaw-thrust technique and finger sweep (shown at left).

Concepts of Athletic Training FOURTH EDITION
Ronald P. Pfeiffer and Brent C. Mangus

Initial Assessment: Breathing

Breathing Assessment

- Conscious athlete is breathing but must be monitored.
- Unconscious athlete can be assessed quickly, ONCE airway is opened.

- Look, listen, and feel for air flow.

Notes

Concepts of Athletic Training FOURTH EDITION

Initial Survey: Circulation Assessment

- Responsive athlete who is breathing will have signs of circulation.
- If athlete is unresponsive, breathing, coughing, and movement in response to breaths are signs of circulation.
- If there are no signs of circulation, **begin CPR**.

Concepts of Athletic Training FOURTH EDITION

Initial Survey: Hemorrhage Assessment

Most external bleeding is obvious.

- Control with direct pressure, elevation, pressure points, and/or pressure bandage.
  -- Take precautions against bloodborne pathogens.

Internal hemorrhage is difficult to detect.

Concepts of Athletic Training FOURTH EDITION

Initial Survey: Hemorrhage Assessment (continued)

An early sign of internal hemorrhage is hypovolemic shock. Signs include:
- Rapid weak pulse.
- Rapid shallow breathing.
- Moist clammy-feeling skin.
- Blue inside lips and under nail beds.

Shock is a true medical emergency.

_____

_____

_____

_____

_____

_____

_____

_____

_____

_____

_____

types of shock

_____

_____

_____

Concepts of Athletic Training FOURTH EDITION
Ronald P. Pfeiffer and Brent C. Mangus

Physical Exam

Observation
- Note signs and symptoms relating to the injury.
- Note athlete's body position and behavior.
- Look and feel for signs of injury.
- Perform D-O-T-S assessment.

Concepts of Athletic Training FOURTH EDITION
Ronald P. Pfeiffer and Brent C. Mangus

Shock

Signs and symptoms include:
- Profuse sweating.
- Cool, clammy-feeling skin.
- Dilated pupils.
- Elevated pulse and respiration.
- Irritable behavior.
- Extreme thirst.
- Nausea and/or vomiting.

Concepts of Athletic Training FOURTH EDITION
Ronald P. Pfeiffer and Brent C. Mangus

Treating Shock

- Have athlete lie down (supine) with legs elevated about 8 to 12 inches.
- Cover the athlete with a blanket.
- Monitor vital signs.
- If spinal injury is suspected, do not move the athlete.

Notes

Taking Medical History

- Keep questions simple and brief—"yes" or "no" answers.
- Use easy-to-understand terms; avoid leading questions.
- Coach should maintain his or her composure.
- Ask athlete what happened. Ask if there were any strange sounds when injury occurred. If athlete is in pain, ask where it hurts.
- Inquire about previous injuries to involved area.
- Pass history on to medical personnel.

Palpation

Palpation is:

- A useful skill if practiced to find deformity, spasm, swelling, etc.
- A learned skill that requires physical contact with the athlete.
- Carefully done to avoid aggravating existing injuries.
- Begun by palpating away from areas of injury.
- Begun with the uninjured limb, if the injury is an extremity.

Removal from Field or Court

- If athlete is conscious and has no injuries that preclude walking, he/she may leave field under own power but with assistance.
- If lower-extremity injury is present, use passive transport system.
- If athlete is unconscious or may have neck injury:
    - Stay with athlete.
    - Monitor vital signs.
    - Treat for shock.
    - Summon EMS.
- Unless athlete is likely to be injured further, **do not move** prior to EMS arrival.

Return to Play?

Ronald P. Pfeiffer and Brent C. Mangus
Concepts of Athletic Training FOURTH EDITION

- Athletes with neurologic injury should not be allowed to return until evaluated by trained medical personnel.

- Athletes suffering from heat-related problems should be removed from participation and cleared for return only by medical professional.

Ronald P. Pfeiffer and Brent C. Mangus
Concepts of Athletic Training FOURTH EDITION

The Coach's Limitations

- Coaches must take special care **NOT** to overstep their bounds when managing an injury.

- Coaches should only provide first aid care and should avoid performing any procedure that is clearly the domain of allied health personnel.

Q's

No

Yes 1,2,4,5,6,7,8,

et all

Notes

Chapter 8

The Injury Process

The Physics of Sports Injury

Connective Tissue

- Connective tissues are the most common type of tissue in the body.
- Connective tissues include ligaments, retinaculum, joint capsules, bone, cartilage, fascia, and tendons.
- In some sports, nearly 50% of acute injuries involve either tendon or muscle.

The Physics of Sports Injury (continued)

Muscle/fascia are thought to be injured by excessive tension during eccentric contractions.

- Tendons are strong; strains occur most often at the distal musculotendinous junction (MTJ).
- Musculotendinous strains are the most common soft tissue sports injuries.

Notes

_____

_____

_____

_____

_____

_____

_____

_____

_____

_____

_____

_____

_____

_____

_____

_____

_____

_____

_____

_____

_____

_____

_____

_____

_____

_____

_____

_____

_____

_____

_____

_____

_____

_____

_____

_____

Mechanical Forces of Injury

Types of Force

- Compressive

- Tensile

- Shear

Mechanical Forces of Injury (continued)

- Tendons resist tensile forces.
- Bones resist compressive forces.
- Ligaments resist tensile forces.

Each type of tissue has a limit for how much force it can withstand (**critical force**).

The Physiology of Sports Injury

The inflammatory process:

- Is a predictable sequence of physiologic actions that occur when the body reacts to repair damaged tissues.

- Begins during the first few minutes following an injury.

The body's initial response to trauma is commonly called swelling.

Notes

Ronald P. Pfeiffer and Brent C. Mangus
Concepts of Athletic Training FOURTH EDITION

The Inflammatory Process (continued)

Normal signs and symptoms of inflammation include:

- Swelling.

- Pain.

- Reddening of skin (erythema).

- Increased temperature in the affected area.

Ronald P. Pfeiffer and Brent C. Mangus
Concepts of Athletic Training FOURTH EDITION

Acute Inflammatory Phase

- Trauma destroys millions of cells.
- Vasoconstriction is followed by vasodilation.
- Damage to blood vessels results in blood flow into interstitial spaces causing hematoma.
- Hematoma is "localized collection of extravasted blood."
- Secondary hypoxic injury results in additional cellular destruction.

Ronald P. Pfeiffer and Brent C. Mangus
Concepts of Athletic Training FOURTH EDITION

Acute Inflammatory Phase (continued)

In response to injury, chemicals are released that affect nearby cells. The effects of these chemicals are:
- **Degradative** (cellular breakdown).

- **Vasoactive** (vasodilators).

- **Chemotactic** (attract scavenger cells).

Ronald P. Pfeiffer and Brent C. Mangus
Concepts of Athletic Training FOURTH EDITION

Acute Inflammatory Phase (continued)

Hageman Factor is responsible for the manufacture of bradykinin.

- **Bradykinin** increases vascular permeability and triggers the release of prostaglandins resulting in:
  - Vasodilation.
  - Increased vascular permeability.
  - Pain.
  - Blood clotting.

Ronald P. Pfeiffer and Brent C. Mangus
Concepts of Athletic Training FOURTH EDITION

Acute Inflammatory Phase (continued)

- Plasma proteins, platelets, and leukocytes move out of capillaries and into damaged tissue.
- Leukocytes engage in phagocytosis.
- Macrophages migrate into the damaged area. Arachidonic acid is formed by a combination of leukocyte enzymes and phospholipids derived from cell membranes.
- Arachidonic acid catalyzes the production of leukotrienes.

Ronald P. Pfeiffer and Brent C. Mangus
Concepts of Athletic Training FOURTH EDITION

Acute Inflammatory Phase (continued)

The acute inflammatory process results in walling off the damaged area from the rest of the body.

The mass of cellular debris, enzymes, and chemical attractants serves to clean up the debris and provide components for healing.

The acute phase lasts up to 3 or 4 days, unless aggravated by additional trauma.

Resolution (Healing) Phase

During this phase, special **leukocytes** (polymorphs and monocytes) and a type of macrophage (histocytes) migrate into the area of injury.

- These cells break down cellular debris and set the stage for regeneration and repair.

Regeneration and Repair

Except for bone, connective tissues heal with scar tissue that begins to form 3-4 days after the injury.

- Fibroblasts (proteoglycan- and collagen-producing cells) migrate into the damaged area.
- Fibroblasts are immature connective tissue cells that can mature into several types of cells.

Regeneration and Repair (continued)

- **Angiogenesis** is the formation of new capillaries.

- **Scar formation** may take four months.

  - Scar can be 95% as strong as original tissue. Stress is helpful for rehabilitation; exercises are critical to this process.
  - Bone tissue heals by way of specialized cells (osteoclasts and osteoblasts).

Notes

Ronald P. Pfeiffer and Brent C. Mangus
Concepts of Athletic Training FOURTH EDITION

Pain and Acute Injury

- Everyone copes with pain differently.
- Pain is as much psychological as physiological.
- Pain results from sensory input received through the nervous system and indicates location of tissue damage.
- Messages concerning sensory information that travel quickly through nervous system are given higher priority than pain messages that travel more slowly.
- Pain is not a useful indicator of injury severity.

Ronald P. Pfeiffer and Brent C. Mangus
Concepts of Athletic Training FOURTH EDITION

Intervention Procedures

Sports medicine community has no clear set of criteria for first aid treatment of acute soft-tissue injury.

Cryotherapy includes bags of crushed ice, aerosol coolants, ice cups, ice water bath immersion, and commercial cold packs.

After the acute phase, thermotherapy is appropriate (i.e., hydrocolator packs, moist warm towels, and ultrasound diathermy).

Ronald P. Pfeiffer and Brent C. Mangus
Concepts of Athletic Training FOURTH EDITION

Intervention Procedures (continued)

- Modalities such as ultrasound should **ONLY** be used under the supervision of trained allied health personnel.
- Pharmacologic agents can be used, such as anti-inflammatories and analgesics.
  - If prescribed by a physician, these agents represent treatments that are beyond the scope of coach.
- OTC drugs should also be used with caution. (Consult parents when athlete is under 18 years of age.)

Concepts of Athletic Training FOURTH EDITION
Ronald P. Pfeiffer and Brent C. Mangus

Cryotherapy

- Direct application of cold may reduce vasodilation in the first few minutes after injury.
- Application of cold can decrease recovery time by reducing cells' metabolic activity.

Concepts of Athletic Training FOURTH EDITION
Ronald P. Pfeiffer and Brent C. Mangus

Cryotherapy (continued)

- In extremities, elevation and compression are also helpful.
- Crushed ice in a plastic bag is an inexpensive technique.
- Elastic wrap secures the ice bag to the body.
- Cold application has analgesic effect and reduces muscle spasm.
- Recommended protocol: Apply for 30 minutes, remove for 2 hours, and re-apply for another 30 minutes, if needed.
- Risk of frostbite is minimal.

Concepts of Athletic Training FOURTH EDITION
Ronald P. Pfeiffer and Brent C. Mangus

Thermotherapy

Thermotherapeutic agents:

- Should **NEVER** be applied to an acute injury.
- Increase vasodilation.
- Are useful in the final stages of injury repair.

Notes

Ronald P. Pfeiffer and Brent C. Mangus
Concepts of Athletic Training FOURTH EDITION

Pharmacologic Agents

Steroidal and non-steroidal anti-inflammatory drugs (**NSAIDs**)
- Both interfere with the inflammatory process.
- Steroidal drugs resemble gluococorticoids, but the exact mechanism of their action is unknown.

Steroids may:
- Decrease amount of chemicals released by lysosomes.
- Decrease permeability of capillaries.
- Reduce WBC phagocytosis.
- Reduce local fever.

Ronald P. Pfeiffer and Brent C. Mangus
Concepts of Athletic Training FOURTH EDITION

Pharmacologic Agents (continued)

Steroids must be used with care.
- They can interfere with collagen formation, decreasing connective tissue strength in injured area.

Steroids may be injected or taken orally and include drugs such as:
- Cortisone, hydrocortisone, prednisone, prednisolone, triamcinolone, and dexamethasone.

Ronald P. Pfeiffer and Brent C. Mangus
Concepts of Athletic Training FOURTH EDITION

Pharmacologic Agents (continued)

NSAIDs do not have the negative effects of steroids.

- NSAIDs are very popular drugs.

- Common NSAIDs include aspirin, ibuprofen, naproxen, indomethacin, and naproxen sodium.

Ronald P. Pfeiffer and Brent C. Mangus

Concepts of Athletic Training FOURTH EDITION

NSAIDs (continued)

- NSAIDs block the conversion of arachidonic acid to prostaglandin.

- Aspirin has anti-inflammatory, analgesic, and antipyretic effects.

- Research is inconclusive regarding NSAIDs effect on tissue healing and strength.

Ronald P. Pfeiffer and Brent C. Mangus

Concepts of Athletic Training FOURTH EDITION

R.I.C.E.

Best approach to the care of soft tissue injury is **RICE** along with prescribed pharmacologic agents and supervised rehabilitative exercise.

- R = Rest
- I = Ice
- C = Compression
- E = Elevation

Ronald P. Pfeiffer and Brent C. Mangus

Concepts of Athletic Training FOURTH EDITION

The Role of Exercise Rehabilitation

- Properly supervised physical activity is most effective for many injuries.
- Such exercise can have a positive effect on collagen formation.

Notes

_____

_____

_____

_____

_____

_____

_____

_____

_____

_____

_____

_____

_____

_____

_____

_____

_____

_____

_____

_____

_____

_____

_____

_____

Ronald P. Pfeiffer and Brent C. Mangus
Concepts of Athletic Training FOURTH EDITION

Exercise Rehabilitation

- Collagen formation and tissue regeneration requires 2 to 3 weeks.

- Rehabilitation must be supervised by professionals with appropriate training, such as a NATABOC-certified Athletic Trainer or a Physical Therapist with sports medicine training.

Ronald P. Pfeiffer and Brent C. Mangus
Concepts of Athletic Training FOURTH EDITION

Exercise Rehabilitation (continued)

Rehabilitative exercise is a four-phase process.
- Passive exercise
- Active assisted
- Active exercise
- Resistive

Q's

No

Yes 1, 3, 4, 5, 8, 9, 11, 13, 14, 15, 16
20, 24, 25, 26

Notes

Chapter 9

Injuries to the Head, Neck, and Face

Anatomy Review

Skull
- The skull has 8 cranial bones & 14 facial bones.
- Cranial bones have articulations called suture joints.

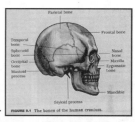

FIGURE 9.1 The bones of the human cranium.

Anatomy Review (continued)

- Soft tissue structures protect the cranium.

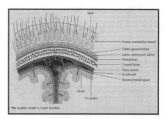

Notes

Anatomy Review (continued)

The Meninges

- Located underneath cranial bones, consisting the dura, arachnoid, and pia mater.

Anatomy Review (continued)

- Dura mater is dense and highly vascularized.
- Arachnoid (middle layer) is less dense and avascular.
- Sub-arachnoid space contains CSF.
    CSF cushions the CNS from external forces.
- Pia mater (innermost layer) is thin, delicate, and highly vascularized.

Anatomy Review (continued)

Central Nervous System (CNS)
- Brain (encephalon) and spinal cord comprise the CNS.
- CNS is protected by meninges, cranium, and vertebrae.
- CNS consists of gray and white matter and weighs 3.0 to 3.5 lbs (adult).
- Brain has three basic components, the cerebrum, cerebellum, and brain stem.
- Neural impulses travel via 12 pairs of cranial nerves and 31 pairs of spinal nerves.

Notes

_____
_____
_____
_____
_____
_____
_____
_____
_____
_____
_____
_____
_____
_____
_____
_____
_____
_____
_____
_____
_____
_____
_____
_____
_____
_____
_____
_____
_____
_____
_____
_____
_____
_____
_____
_____
_____
_____

Ronald P. Pfeiffer and Brent C. Mangus
Concepts of Athletic Training FOURTH EDITION

Anatomy Review (continued)

The Face
- The face is comprised of skin placed over underlying bones.
  - Subcutaneous muscles, cartilage, and fat provide minor protection.
- Several areas of the face are prone to injury, particularly orbits of the eyes, nasal bones, and mandible.

Ronald P. Pfeiffer and Brent C. Mangus
Concepts of Athletic Training FOURTH EDITION

Anatomy Review (continued)

The Neck (cervical spine)
- The 7 cervical vertebrae provide support for the head and protection for the spinal cord.

Ronald P. Pfeiffer and Brent C. Mangus
Concepts of Athletic Training FOURTH EDITION

Anatomy Review (continued)

- The first cervical vertebra (C-1) is called atlas.
  - Atlas articulates with the occipital bone to form R and L atlanto-occipital joints.
  - The second cervical vertebra (C-2) is called axis.
- The skull and C-1 articulate as a unit with C-2 to form the atlantoaxial joint.

Notes

_____

_____

_____

_____

_____

_____

_____

_____

_____

_____

_____

_____

_____

_____

_____

_____

_____

_____

_____

_____

_____

_____

_____

_____

_____

_____

_____

_____

_____

_____

_____

_____

_____

_____

_____

_____

_____

_____

Ronald P. Pfeiffer and Brent C. Mangus

Concepts of Athletic Training FOURTH EDITION

Head Injuries in Sports

Even minor head trauma can result in serious injury.

- Brain tissue is unable to repair itself; any tissue loss results in some level of permanent disability.
- Severe injuries can result in death.
- Coaches can learn to recognize head injuries and render first aid when necessary.

Ronald P. Pfeiffer and Brent C. Mangus

Concepts of Athletic Training FOURTH EDITION

Mechanisms of Head Injury

Direct injury to the head involves a blow to the head that causes injury at impact site.
- Contrecoup injury
- Coup injury

Indirect injury to the head results from damaging forces traveling to the head from other parts of the body.

Treat every head injury as if there is a neck injury and vice versa.

Ronald P. Pfeiffer and Brent C. Mangus

Concepts of Athletic Training FOURTH EDITION

Head Injuries in Sports

Cranial injury:

- Involves the bones of the skull.
- May be associated soft tissue injury.

Depressed skull fracture:

- Involves bone fragments being pushed into the cranial region.

Notes

Ronald P. Pfeiffer and Brent C. Mangus

Concepts of Athletic Training FOURTH EDITION

Head Injuries in Sports (continued)

Concussion is "a clinical syndrome characterized by immediate and transient impairment of neurologic function secondary to mechanical forces."

- Symptoms include unconsciousness, disorientation, headache, amnesia, dizziness, and disequilibrium.

Ronald P. Pfeiffer and Brent C. Mangus

Concepts of Athletic Training FOURTH EDITION

Head Injuries in Sports (continued)

Cantu classification

- Grade 1 involves no amnesia but are difficult to identify.
- Grade 2 involves loss of consciousness for less than 1 minute and/or PTA lasting longer than 30 minutes.
- Grade 3 involves loss of consciousness for more than a minute and PTA lasting more than 24 hours.

Anterograde vs. retrograde amnesia

Ronald P. Pfeiffer and Brent C. Mangus

Concepts of Athletic Training FOURTH EDITION

Head Injuries in Sports (continued)

Second Impact Syndrome (SIS) can be a serious problem.

- Results when an athlete with a head injury receives another head injury before the symptoms of the first injury have resolved.
- Involves rapid and catastrophic brain swelling.
- SIS can result in death.

Any athlete sustaining a head injury, no matter how minor, should be monitored by a physician before being cleared to return to participation.

Intracranial Injury

- These injuries are potentially life threatening.

- Majority result from blunt trauma.

- Disruption of blood vessels results in intra-cranial bleeding (hematoma) and swelling within the cranium.

Intracranial Injuries

Major forms of intracranial injury include:
- Epidural hematoma.
- Subdural hematoma.
- Intracerebral hematoma.
- Cerebral contusion.

Epidural hematoma develops quickly due to arterial bleeding, while subdural hematoma develops slowly due to venous bleeding.

Some degree of permanent neurologic damage and even death can result.

Initial Survey

Stabilizing the athlete's head and neck

Always assume a neck injury has also occurred.
- **Check vitals first.**
- **Note body and limb positions, as well as helmet, face mask, and mouth guard positions.**
- If unconscious, attempt to arouse and note approx. time of injury.
- Immobilize head and neck immediately; do not remove athlete's helmet.

Notes

Ronald P. Pfeiffer and Brent C. Mangus
Concepts of Athletic Training *FOURTH EDITION*

Initial Survey (continued)

- If unconscious, detect breathing by:
  - Listening near the athlete's face for typical breathing sounds.
  - Looking for movements of the thorax and/or abdomen.

If no signs of circulation are present, begin CPR and summon EMS.

Ronald P. Pfeiffer and Brent C. Mangus
Concepts of Athletic Training *FOURTH EDITION*

Physical Examination

The physical exam must include assessments of:

- Consciousness or unconsciousness.
- Extremity strength without moving the neck, if conscious.
- Mental function, if conscious.
- Signs and movements.
- Neck pain.
- Neck spasm.

Ronald P. Pfeiffer and Brent C. Mangus
Concepts of Athletic Training *FOURTH EDITION*

Physical Exam (continued)

If head injury is suspected:

- Don't remove helmet.
- Don't move.
- Don't arouse someone with ammonia capsules.
- Don't rush through physical exam.
- If athlete is conscious, use quick neurological tests, such as grip strength and skin sensation.
- Examine the eyes, noting pupil size, responsiveness to light, and side-to-side movement.
- Palpate the neck for deformity.

Ronald P. Pfeiffer and Brent C. Mangus
Concepts of Athletic Training FOURTH EDITION

Physical Exam (continued)

If athlete is conscious:
- Perform grip strength tests.
- Check bilateral strength by asking athlete to dorsiflex feet.
- Check for sensations on both sides of body by pinch tests.
- Monitor athlete's eyes by checking pupil sizes and response to light, and eyes' ability to follow moving object.
- Note loss of peripheral vision or jerking eyeball movements.
- Palpate neck, moving from base of skull to bottom of neck.

Ronald P. Pfeiffer and Brent C. Mangus
Concepts of Athletic Training FOURTH EDITION

Physical Exam (continued)

Based on these observations, determine level of consciousness.
- Athlete with grade 1 concussion should be able to walk with assistance.
- Athlete with grade 2 or 3 concussion should not be moved.
  - Monitor vital signs.
  - Summon EMS.

Any athlete with a concussion should be removed from field of play and examined by a physician.

Ronald P. Pfeiffer and Brent C. Mangus
Concepts of Athletic Training FOURTH EDITION

Quick Neurological Tests

Finger-to-Nose Test   Romberg's Test

Notes

_____
_____
_____
_____
_____
_____
_____
_____
_____
_____
_____
_____
_____
_____
_____
_____
_____
_____
_____
_____
_____
_____
_____
_____
_____
_____
_____
_____
_____
_____
_____
_____
_____
_____
_____
_____

Ronald P. Pfeiffer and Brent C. Mangus
Concepts of Athletic Training FOURTH EDITION

Cervical Spine Injuries

Neck Injuries
- Majority occur in football, rugby, ice hockey, soccer, diving, and gymnastics. Cervical injuries, however, can occur in almost any sport.

- Catastrophic injuries are rare--less than 2 in 100,000 of all neck injuries reported in the United States.

Ronald P. Pfeiffer and Brent C. Mangus
Concepts of Athletic Training FOURTH EDITION

Cervical Spine Injuries (continued)

- Mechanisms include hyperflexion, hyperextension, rotation, lateral flexion, and axial loading.

- Neck strains rarely involve neurologic damage.

- Serious injuries occur when intact vertebra or fragments of fractured vertebra are displaced or an intervertebral disk ruptures and places pressure on spinal cord or nerve roots.

Ronald P. Pfeiffer and Brent C. Mangus
Concepts of Athletic Training FOURTH EDITION

Mechanism of Cervical Spine Injuries

- Axial load produces most cervical spine injuries.
- 1976 NCAA enacted the rule barring "spearing."
- Any forced movement of cervical spine can result in injury.
- Brachial plexus injuries can produce significant, but transient symptoms.

Coaching personnel must take great care when conducting an examination of an athlete suspected of having a neck injury.

Notes

Concepts of Athletic Training FOURTH EDITION

General Treatment Guidelines

- Neck sprains

- Neck strains

- Neck fractures and dislocations

Concepts of Athletic Training FOURTH EDITION

Initial Treatment of Neck Injury

- Medical care team leader supervises the process.
- Determine if the athlete is conscious. If unconscious, check airway, breathing, and pulse (circulation).
- Summon EMS.
- Continue monitoring "ABCs."

Concepts of Athletic Training FOURTH EDITION

Initial Treatment of Injury Guidelines

- If conscious, question the athlete regarding extremity numbness or loss of feeling, weakness, and/or neck pain.

- If athlete reports the inability to move a limb or limbs or significant strength loss, stabilize head and neck and summon EMS.

Concepts of Athletic Training FOURTH EDITION
Ronald P. Pfeiffer and Brent C. Mangus

Initial Treatment of Neck Injury (continued)

If EMS arrival is delayed, place the injured athlete on a properly constructed spine board.

- This requires the coordinated effort of at least 5 people.

Concepts of Athletic Training FOURTH EDITION
Ronald P. Pfeiffer and Brent C. Mangus

Spine Boarding an Athlete

1
2
3
4

Concepts of Athletic Training FOURTH EDITION
Ronald P. Pfeiffer and Brent C. Mangus

Removal of Athlete's Helmet

- Management of the helmeted player is a major issue.

  Football head and face protective equipment create special problems.

  In cases involving neck injury, a football helmet provides cervical immobilization.

Notes

_____

_____

_____

_____

_____

_____

_____

_____

_____

_____

_____

_____

_____

_____

_____

_____

_____

_____

_____

_____

_____

_____

_____

_____

_____

_____

_____

_____

_____

_____

_____

_____

_____

_____

Ronald P. Pfeiffer and Brent C. Mangus
Concepts of Athletic Training FOURTH EDITION

Football Face Mask Removal

IIf airway must be established, removal of the face mask is necessary.

Cut the clips with a device like the "Trainer's Angel."

Once the clips are removed, the face mask can be rolled up, and out of the way of the airway.

If Trainer's Angel is not available, removal of screws that hold the clips with a screwdriver is an option.

Ronald P. Pfeiffer and Brent C. Mangus
Concepts of Athletic Training FOURTH EDITION

Injuries to the Maxillofacial Region

- Maxillofacial injuries include those to the jaw, teeth, eyes, ears, nose, throat, facial bones, and skin.
- Modern protective equipment has reduced significantly the incidence of these injuries. Such equipment includes:
    - Mouth guards.
    - Protective eye wear.
    - Face shields.

Ronald P. Pfeiffer and Brent C. Mangus
Concepts of Athletic Training FOURTH EDITION

Injuries to the Maxillofacial Region (continued)

Dental Injuries

- Jaw has 32 teeth.
- Teeth are vulnerable to external blows that are common in many sports.
- Teeth are secured by cementum and periosteum.

Ronald P. Pfeiffer and Brent C. Mangus
Concepts of Athletic Training FOURTH EDITION
Injuries to the Maxillofacial Region (continued)

- Majority of dental injuries result from direct blows that result in tooth displacement, a fracture and avulsion, and fracture of jaw or other facial bones.
- When rendering first aid, take precautions to avoid bloodborne pathogens.
- When examining dental injuries:
  - Can athlete open and close mouth without pain?
  - What is the general symmetry of the teeth?
  - Are there any irregularities in adjacent teeth?
  - Is there bleeding, especially along gum line?

Ronald P. Pfeiffer and Brent C. Mangus
Concepts of Athletic Training FOURTH EDITION
Injuries to the Maxillofacial Region (continued)

Loosened or knocked-out tooth:
- Gently push back into place.
- If knocked out, place in sterile saline and refer athlete to dentist or physician immediately.

High risk sports should require use of mouth guard.
- Required for high school football players since 1966; NCAA followed suit in 1974.
- Three types of guards are stock, mouth-formed, and custom fitted.

Ronald P. Pfeiffer and Brent C. Mangus
Concepts of Athletic Training FOURTH EDITION
Eye Injuries

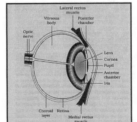

- Eye consists of a ball-like structure housed within the orbit.

- Globe is filled with vitreous body.

Notes

Concepts of Athletic Training FOURTH EDITION

Eye Injuries (continued)

The posterior interior surface is covered by the retina.

Most of the eyeball is encased in the sclera.

Eye injuries in the U.S. are on the increase; basketball, baseball, and softball are leading sports for eye injuries. Racket sports are also responsible for eye injuries.

Proper position of the fingers for an initial examination of the eye

Concepts of Athletic Training FOURTH EDITION

Eye Injuries (continued)

Two categories of eye injuries are contusional and penetrating.

- Contusional injuries vary in severity from simple corneal abrasions to major injuries such as rupture of the eye, fracture of orbit, or combinations of the two. Detached retina can also occur.
- Penetrating injuries are less common than contusional injuries. May occur in shooting sports or when eye protective equipment is defective.

Concepts of Athletic Training FOURTH EDITION

Eye Injuries (continued)

Initial Evaluation and Treatment Guidelines

- Majority of injuries are simple corneal abrasions or small foreign object in eye.
- Hold upper eyelid away from anterior eye.
- Small foreign bodies usually found below lower eyelid or in the medial canthus.
- Visible foreign object can be removed with a moist cotton swab, if imbedded, cover both eyes and transport to medical facility.

Notes

Ronald P. Pfeiffer and Brent C. Mangus
Concepts of Athletic Training FOURTH EDITION

Eye Injuries (continued)

- If nothing can be seen in the eye, injury is probably a corneal abrasion.
- Contusions may result in hemorrhage around the eye known as a "black eye."
- More severe cases may involve bleeding into the anterior eye ("hyphema") and orbital blowout. Refer to medical facility immediately.
  - Symptoms of orbital blowout include eye pain, double vision (diplopia), and obvious bleeding within the eye.

Ronald P. Pfeiffer and Brent C. Mangus
Concepts of Athletic Training FOURTH EDITION

Eye Injuries (continued)

Retinal injuries develop slowly. Early symptoms include:
- Floating particles in field of vision.
- Distorted vision.
- Changes in the amount of light seen.

Any athlete with a history of blunt trauma to the eye who later complains of these symptoms should be referred immediately for medical evaluation.

Ronald P. Pfeiffer and Brent C. Mangus
Concepts of Athletic Training FOURTH EDITION

Eye Injuries (continued)

Contact Lens Problems
- Many athletes wear contacts with few problems; however, more problems occur with hard lenses.
- Major problems include having a lens slip out of place or debris become trapped between the lens and the eye.
- Coach should have first aid kit to treat common contact problems including: wetting solution, small mirror, and contact-lens case.

Protective eyewear is strongly recommended.

Notes

_____

_____

_____

_____

_____

_____

_____

_____

_____

_____

_____

_____

_____

_____

_____

_____

_____

_____

_____

_____

_____

_____

_____

_____

_____

_____

_____

_____

_____

_____

_____

_____

Ronald P. Pfeiffer and Brent C. Mangus

Concepts of Athletic Training *FOURTH EDITION*

Injuries to the Maxillofacial Region

Nose Injuries

- The nose is often injured because of its location; bloody nose (epistaxis) may be the most common facial injury in sports.
- Anatomically, nose is a bone-cartilage framework with skin attached. Nasal bones include R & L nasal bones and the frontal processes of the maxilla.
- Inside the nose, the two nostrils are separated by the cartilaginous septum.

Ronald P. Pfeiffer and Brent C. Mangus

Concepts of Athletic Training *FOURTH EDITION*

Nose Injuries (continued)

Evaluation & Treatment Guidelines
- Any blow to the nose can cause a fracture.
  Signs are a nosebleed and deformity and swelling at the bridge of the nose.
- If a fracture is suspected, control the nosebleed and refer to a medical doctor.
  - Finger pressure applied directly against the nostril that is bleeding can control simple nosebleed. Wear gloves to avoid contact with blood.

Ronald P. Pfeiffer and Brent C. Mangus

Concepts of Athletic Training *FOURTH EDITION*

Nose Injuries (continued)

Care of a nose bleed includes:
- Application of a cold compress against the nasal region.
- Having the athlete lie on side—the same side as bleeding nostril.
- Can pack nostril with gauze that protrudes from nostril.

Be alert to the presence of septal hematoma:
- Can lead to septal erosion.
- Must be referred to medical doctor for evaluation and treatment.

Concepts of Athletic Training *FOURTH EDITION*

Ear Injuries

Anatomy of the Ear

- Ear has a cartilaginous framework covered with a layer of skin.
- The external ear has large expanded portion (auricula) and opening to ear canal (external acoustic meatus).
- The middle ear contains small group of bones that transmit sound vibrations to tympanic membrane.
- Inner ear contains the labyrinth that has a role in equilibrium.

Concepts of Athletic Training *FOURTH EDITION*

Injuries to the Ear (continued)

- Majority of ear problems are related to the external ear.
- Sports such as wrestling are involved in ear problems because of contact with opponents and/or playing surface.
  - Such contact can result in abrasions and contusions to auricle.
  - Required head gear has reduced incidence of such injuries.
- Auricle has some vascularity and can develop a hematoma leading to cauliflower ear.

Concepts of Athletic Training *FOURTH EDITION*

Injuries to the Ear (continued)

- Auricular hematoma should be treated with cold pack and immediately referred to a medical doctor.
- Severe blows to the outer ear can result in a ruptured ear drum.
- Athletes with ear infections should not participate in aquatic sports until infection has resolved.

Notes

_____

_____

_____

_____

_____

_____

_____

_____

_____

_____

_____

_____

_____

_____

_____

_____

_____

_____

_____

_____

_____

_____

_____

_____

_____

_____

_____

_____

_____

_____

_____

Ronald P. Pfeiffer and Brent C. Mangus
Concepts of Athletic Training FOURTH EDITION

Injuries to the Maxillofacial Region

Fractures of the Face
- In collision sports, mandible is common site of injury.
- Signs and symptoms include:
  - Pain and swelling.
  - Deformity and malocclusion.

Ronald P. Pfeiffer and Brent C. Mangus
Concepts of Athletic Training FOURTH EDITION

Jaw Dislocation

Signs and symptoms include:
- Extreme pain and deformity in the region of the temporomandibular joint.
- Inability to move lower jaw.
- Jaw is "locked."
- Do NOT attempt to put back into place.
- Treatment includes application of ice pack and medical referral.
- Zygomatic bone may be fractured.

Ronald P. Pfeiffer and Brent C. Mangus
Concepts of Athletic Training FOURTH EDITION

Jaw Dislocation (continued)

Signs and symptoms of zygomatic bone fractures include:

- Pain and swelling at site of injury.
- Swelling and discoloration spreads to the region of the orbit.

Refer athlete to a physician for diagnosis and treatment.

Ronald P. Pfeiffer and Brent C. Mangus
Concepts of Athletic Training FOURTH EDITION

Wounds of the Facial Region

Facial wounds can take many forms and treatment should follow basic first aid protocol.

- Carefully clean with mild soap and warm water; apply sterile dressing.
- Any facial wound, even abrasion, can present cosmetic problems.
- Refer to a physician.

Ronald P. Pfeiffer and Brent C. Mangus
Concepts of Athletic Training FOURTH EDITION

Facial Wounds (continued)

- In general, any wound with observable space between margins should be seen by a physician for suturing.
- After suturing, the return-to-play decision is made by the physician.

Q's

No

Yes 2, 3, 4, 6, 7, 8, 11, 12, 13, 15, 16, 17, 20, 21, 25,

Notes

Concepts of
Athletic Training FOURTH EDITION
Ronald P. Pfeiffer
Brent C. Mangus

Chapter 10

Injuries to the Thoracic Through Coccygeal Spine

Ronald P. Pfeiffer and Brent C. Mangus
Concepts of Athletic Training FOURTH EDITION

Anatomy Review of the Thoracic Spine

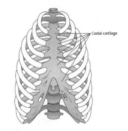

Costal cartilage

- Thoracic spine is comprised of 12 vertebrae that articulate with the cervical and lumbar spines.
- The thoracic spine, corresponding 12 pairs of ribs, and sternum form the thoracic cage.

Ronald P. Pfeiffer and Brent C. Mangus
Concepts of Athletic Training FOURTH EDITION

Common Sports Injuries

Skeletal Injuries of the Thoracic Vertebrae

- Compression fractures of the vertebral body are most common injury.
- Such fractures usually occur at junction of thoracic and lumbar spine.
- Athlete with recent history of trauma to the region in conjunction with pain or numbness should be referred to a physician.
- Scheuermann's disease is adolescent condition characterized by kyphosis. Children with chronic thoracic pain should be evaluated.

Notes

Concepts of Athletic Training FOURTH EDITION

Common Sports Injuries (continued)

- Posterior rib fractures can result in a pneumothorax.

- Such fractures are associated with direct blows to lateral or posterior thorax and can occur anywhere along the rib, commonly fracture near the anatomic angle.

Concepts of Athletic Training FOURTH EDITION

Rib Fractures

Signs and symptoms include:

- Painful respiration.
- Deformity in the region of the injury, including a protruding rib or depression where the normal contour of the rib should be.
- Swelling and discoloration.
- Pain when rib cage is gently compressed.

In severe cases, complications such as pneumothorax or hemopneumothorax can occur.

Concepts of Athletic Training FOURTH EDITION

Rib Fractures (continued)

First Aid

- Immediate application of RICE.

- Treat for shock.

- Refer athlete to physician.

Ronald P. Pfeiffer and Brent C. Mangus

Concepts of Athletic Training FOURTH EDITION

Sprains

Sprains occur whenever a joint is forced beyond its normal ROM.

- Evaluation of a sprain to the thoracic spine is difficult.
- A consistent symptom is painful respiration.

First Aid

- Apply RICE.
- If dyspnea persists for more than 24 hours, refer the athlete to a physician.

Ronald P. Pfeiffer and Brent C. Mangus

Concepts of Athletic Training FOURTH EDITION

Strains

Strains:

- Involve contractile tissue and their support structures, such as the erector spinae and intercostals.
- Are related to maximal exertions.
- Result in muscle spasm and point tenderness.

- **First Aid**
  - Application of RICE.
  - Compression wrap.
  - Referral to a physician.

Ronald P. Pfeiffer and Brent C. Mangus

Concepts of Athletic Training FOURTH EDITION

Lumbar Spine Region

Anatomy Review

- Five vertebrae are in lumbar spine.
- Lumbar vertebrae are the largest moving vertebrae.
- Anterior and posterior longitudinal are the major ligaments.

Notes

_____
_____
_____
_____
_____
_____
_____
_____
_____
_____
_____
_____
_____
_____
_____
_____
_____
_____
_____
_____
_____
_____
_____
_____
_____
_____
_____
_____
_____
_____
_____
_____
_____
_____
_____
_____
_____
_____
_____
_____
_____

Ronald P. Pfeiffer and Brent C. Mangus

Concepts of Athletic Training FOURTH EDITION

Lumbar Spine Region

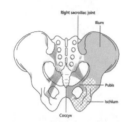

- The sacrum consists of five fused vertebrae.
- Sacrum connects the spinal column to the pelvis.
- Right and left sacroiliac (SI) joints are formed by the union of the sacrum and pelvis.
- Coccyx (tail bone) is most distal portion of the vertebral column.

Ronald P. Pfeiffer and Brent C. Mangus

Concepts of Athletic Training FOURTH EDITION

Spondylolysis and Spondylolisthesis

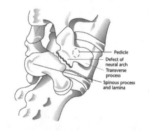

- Spondylolysis is a defect in the neural arch (pars interarticularis). Such defects compromise the articulation between two vertebrae.
- If the condition is bilateral, the affected vertebra can slip forward resulting in spondylolisthesis.

Ronald P. Pfeiffer and Brent C. Mangus

Concepts of Athletic Training FOURTH EDITION

Spondylolysis and Spondylolisthesis (continued)

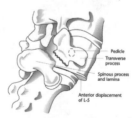

- Symptoms include lower back pain that worsens during hyperextension, and radiating pain to the buttocks and upper thighs.
- Treatment includes rest, drug therapy, lumbar bracing, exclusion from certain sports, and surgery.

Notes

_____

_____

_____

_____

_____

_____

_____

_____

_____

_____

_____

_____

_____

_____

_____

_____

_____

_____

_____

_____

_____

_____

_____

_____

_____

_____

_____

_____

_____

_____

_____

_____

_____

_____

_____

Ronald P. Pfeiffer and Brent C. Mangus
Concepts of Athletic Training FOURTH EDITION

Traumatic Fractures: Lumbar Spine

- Such fractures are uncommon in sports.
- External blows may result in internal injury.
  - Deep abdominal pain, hematuria, and shock are signs and symptoms of internal injury.
  - Immobilize on spine board and transport to medical facility.
- Blows to the coccyx can result from landing on the buttocks.
- Fractures of the coccyx result in severe pain, point tenderness, swelling, and bruising. Refer athlete to physician for evaluation.

Ronald P. Pfeiffer and Brent C. Mangus
Concepts of Athletic Training FOURTH EDITION

Lumbar Region -- Strains & Sprains

- Strains and sprains are the most common soft-tissue injuries to this region.
- Sprains involve ligaments and capsules.
- Major joints include:
  - Lumbosacral.
  - Sacroiliac.
  - Sacrococcygeal.

Ronald P. Pfeiffer and Brent C. Mangus
Concepts of Athletic Training FOURTH EDITION

Lumbar Strains & Sprains (continued)

Signs and symptoms include:

- Local muscle spasm.
- Pain that does not radiate into buttocks or lower extremity.
- Acute postural abnormalities associated with recent trauma.

First Aid

- Have athlete maintain a supine position with soft support for lumbar region and application of ice.
- If not improved in 24 hours, refer to physician.

Concepts of Athletic Training FOURTH EDITION

Lumbar Disk Injuries

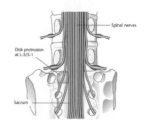

- A serious form of soft tissue injury is "herniated disk."
  - Most commonly occurs at L4 or L5.
- Anatomy of a disk includes annulus fibrosis (outer ring) and nucleus pulposus (inner ring).

Ronald P. Pfeiffer and Brent C. Mangus

Concepts of Athletic Training FOURTH EDITION

Lumbar Disk Injuries (continued)

- Herniation results from a weakened annulus that allows nucleus pulposus to protrude through the wall of the annulus.
- Protrusion may put pressure directly on spinal nerves resulting in:
  - Intense local or radiating pain.
  - Sensory loss or burning/tingling sensation in lower extremity.
  - Muscle spasm and postural abnormalities.

Ronald P. Pfeiffer and Brent C. Mangus

Concepts of Athletic Training FOURTH EDITION

Lumbar Disk Injuries (continued)

First Aid

- Place athlete in supine or most comfortable position. Support lumbar region with rolled towel or other soft material.
- Apply crushed ice to lumbar region.
- Arrange for transport to medical facility.

Q's

NO

Yes 1,2,4,7,8,

Notes

Concepts of Athletic Training FOURTH EDITION
Ronald P. Pfeiffer
Brent C. Mangus

Chapter 11

Injuries to the Shoulder Region

Ronald P. Pfeiffer and Brent C. Mangus
Concepts of Athletic Training FOURTH EDITION

Anatomy Review

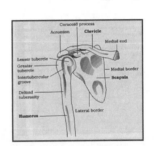

Shoulder bones:
- Consist of shoulder girdle (clavicle & scapula) and humerus.

Shoulder joints:
- Glenohumeral
- Acromioclavicular
- Sternoclavicular

Ronald P. Pfeiffer and Brent C. Mangus
Concepts of Athletic Training FOURTH EDITION

Anatomy (continued)

- Joints are held together with ligaments and joint capsules that provide stability and allow for limited movement.
  - Shoulder girdle and the GH joint can move in almost every direction.
- AC & SC joints are just under the skin and are vulnerable to injury, even in muscular athletes
- Blood supply to the upper extremity originates from branches of the subclavian artery.
- Major nerves are from a group called the brachial plexus.

Notes

_____

_____

_____

_____

_____

_____

_____

_____

_____

_____

_____

_____

_____

_____

_____

_____

_____

_____

_____

_____

_____

_____

_____

_____

_____

_____

_____

_____

_____

_____

_____

_____

_____

_____

_____

_____

_____

_____

_____

Ronald P. Pfeiffer and Brent C. Mangus

Concepts of Athletic Training FOURTH EDITION

Major Arteries of the Arm

This view shows the major arteries stemming from the subclavian artery.

- Not labeled are the anterior and posterior humeral circumflex arteries.

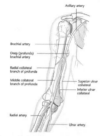

Ronald P. Pfeiffer and Brent C. Mangus

Concepts of Athletic Training FOURTH EDITION

Shoulder Injuries

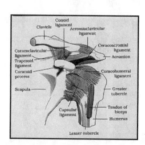

- **Injuries to the shoulder region are common.**
  - AC and SC joint injuries are common in wrestling.
  - Throwing and swinging sports can result in overuse injuries to the rotator cuff.
  - Falls in cycling and skating can result in fractures of the clavicle.
  - Injuries can be either chronic or acute.

Ronald P. Pfeiffer and Brent C. Mangus

Concepts of Athletic Training FOURTH EDITION

The Nerves of the Brachial Plexus

- The major components of the brachial plexus are shown.

- Note the position of the plexus relative to the axillary artery and pectoralis minor.

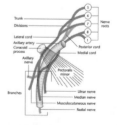

Notes

Ronald P. Pfeiffer and Brent C. Mangus
Concepts of Athletic Training FOURTH EDITION

Fractured Clavicle

Fractures of this bone are the most common fracture in this region.

- This injury usually results from falls or direct blows.
- The adolescent form of this injury is known as a "greenstick" fracture.

All clavicular fractures are potentially dangerous.

Ronald P. Pfeiffer and Brent C. Mangus
Concepts of Athletic Training FOURTH EDITION

Fractured Clavicle (continued)

Signs and symptoms include:

- Swelling.
- Deformity.
- Discoloration.
- Broken bone ends may protrude though skin.

First Aid

- Treat for shock.
- Apply sling & swathe bandage.
- Apply sterile dressings on any wounds.

Ronald P. Pfeiffer and Brent C. Mangus
Concepts of Athletic Training FOURTH EDITION

Fractured Scapula

- Uncommon injury that is normally the result of a direct blow.
- Signs and symptoms are less clear than those for a fractured clavicle.

  Symptoms include:
  - History of severe blow.
  - Considerable pain and functional loss.

- An athlete with such a history and symptoms should be referred to a medical doctor.

Notes

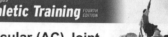

Acromioclavicular (AC) Joint Injuries

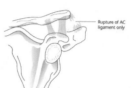

Rupture of AC ligament only

AC joint is located on the lateral superior shoulder, just under the skin.

- Injuries involve AC ligaments & CC ligaments.

AC Joint Injuries (continued)

Typical mechanism is downward blow to the lateral shoulder or fall on an outstretched arm.

- Severity of injury is graded on the amount of damage to ligaments.
  - 1st degree -- no significant ligament damage
  - 2nd degree -- partial tearing of ligaments
  - 3rd degree -- complete rupture

AC Joint Injuries (continued)

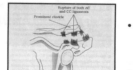

Rupture of both AC and CC ligaments
Prominent clavicle

- Mild swelling with point tenderness.
- Any movement of the shoulder region will be painful.
- In 3rd degree sprain, a snap or pop may have been sensed along with a visible deformity.

Concepts of Athletic Training FOURTH EDITION
Ronald P. Pfeiffer and Brent C. Mangus

AC Joint Injuries (continued)

First Aid

- Treat for shock.
- Apply I.C.E.
- Apply sling & swathe bandage.
- Refer athlete to a physician.

Concepts of Athletic Training FOURTH EDITION
Ronald P. Pfeiffer and Brent C. Mangus

Glenohumeral Joint Injuries

GH joint consists of humeral head and the glenoid fossa of scapula.

- Extremely mobile but inherently unstable joint.
- Major soft tissue structures include capsular ligament and the coracohumeral ligament.
- Typical mechanism of injury is having the arm abducted and externally rotated, stressing the anterior glenohumeral ligament.
- Most common type of location is an anterior dislocation that may be a subluxation or complete dislocation.

Concepts of Athletic Training FOURTH EDITION
Ronald P. Pfeiffer and Brent C. Mangus

Glenohumeral Joint Injuries (continued)

Signs and symptoms include:

- Shoulder joint deformity and down-sloping shoulder contour.
- Abnormally long arm on affected side.
- Humeral head palpable within axilla.
- Athlete supports arm on affected side.
- Athlete resists efforts to move GH joint.

In cases involving subluxation:

- GH joint may appear normal.
- Movement will be painful.
- Joint may be point tender.

Notes

Ronald P. Pfeiffer and Brent C. Mangus

Concepts of Athletic Training FOURTH EDITION

Glenohumeral Joint Injuries (continued)

First Aid

- Treat for shock.
- Application of ice and compression by placing rolled towel into the axilla.
- Apply sling & swathe bandage.
- Refer to a physician immediately.

GH joint injuries tend to be chronic and recur. Surgical treatment may be necessary.

Ronald P. Pfeiffer and Brent C. Mangus

Concepts of Athletic Training FOURTH EDITION

Sternoclavicular Joint Injuries

The sternoclavicular joint is formed by the union of the proximal end of the clavicle and the manubrium of the sternum.

- SC joint is supported by the several ligaments.
- Injuries are rare compared to AC or GH joints.
- Sprains to the SC joint can range in severity.

Mechanism is external blow to the shoulder resulting in a dislocation of proximal clavicle; most commonly, the clavicle moving anteriorly and superiorly.

Ronald P. Pfeiffer and Brent C. Mangus

Concepts of Athletic Training FOURTH EDITION

Sternoclavicular Joint Injuries (continued)

Signs and symptoms include:

- Gross deformity of SC joint (2nd and 3rd degree sprains).
- Swelling & painful movement.
- Snapping or tearing sensations related to the injury.
- Athlete holds arm on affected side close to the body.

First Aid

- Treat for shock.
- Apply ice and compression.
- Sling & swathe bandage.

Notes

_____

_____

_____

_____

_____

_____

_____

_____

_____

_____

_____

_____

_____

_____

_____

_____

_____

_____

_____

_____

_____

_____

_____

_____

_____

_____

_____

_____

_____

_____

_____

_____

_____

_____

_____

_____

_____

Ronald P. Pfeiffer and Brent C. Mangus
Concepts of Athletic Training FOURTH EDITION

Rotator Cuff Strains

- Any muscle of the shoulder can suffer a strain. Most common injury is rotator cuff strain.
- Rotator cuff muscles contribute to GH joint abduction and rotation.
- Errors in the execution of a throw or swing can contribute to overuse injury.

Ronald P. Pfeiffer and Brent C. Mangus
Concepts of Athletic Training FOURTH EDITION

Rotator Cuff Strains

Signs and symptoms include:

- Pain within the shoulder, especially during follow through phase.
- Difficulty bringing arm up and back during cocking phase of throw. Pain and stiffness in shoulder region 12 to 24 hours after throwing or swinging.
- Point tenderness around region of the humeral head that seems to be deep in deltoid muscle.

Ronald P. Pfeiffer and Brent C. Mangus
Concepts of Athletic Training FOURTH EDITION

Rotator Cuff Strains (continued)

First Aid

- First aid is NOT practical due to chronic nature of condition.
- I.C.E.
- Medical referral.

Notes

_____

_____

_____

_____

_____

_____

_____

_____

_____

_____

_____

_____

_____

_____

_____

_____

_____

_____

_____

_____

_____

_____

_____

_____

_____

_____

_____

_____

_____

_____

_____

_____

_____

_____

_____

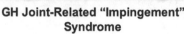
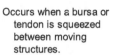

Concepts of Athletic Training FOURTH EDITION
Ronald P. Pfeiffer and Brent C. Mangus

GH Joint-Related "Impingement" Syndrome

Occurs when a bursa or tendon is squeezed between moving structures.

- In cases affecting the GH joint, the tendon of the supraspinatus muscle is commonly impinged.

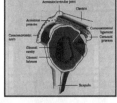

Concepts of Athletic Training FOURTH EDITION
Ronald P. Pfeiffer and Brent C. Mangus

Impingement Syndrome

- Any condition that decreases the size of the subacromial space may result in impingement syndrome.

- Athletes in sports that emphasize overhead arm movements have a high risk of this injury.

Concepts of Athletic Training FOURTH EDITION
Ronald P. Pfeiffer and Brent C. Mangus

Impingement Syndrome (continued)

Signs and symptoms include:

- Pain on abduction & external rotation.
- Strength loss.
- Pain when arm is abducted beyond 80° to 90°.
- Nocturnal pain.
- Pain felt deep within the shoulder.

Notes

Ronald P. Pfeiffer and Brent C. Mangus

Concepts of Athletic Training FOURTH EDITION

Impingement Syndrome (continued)

First Aid

- Rest.
- Anti-inflammatory drugs.
- Physical therapy.
- In extreme cases, surgery.

Ronald P. Pfeiffer and Brent C. Mangus

Concepts of Athletic Training FOURTH EDITION

Biceps Tendon Problems

Note anatomic relationships between long head of the biceps tendon and the GH joint capsule, transverse humeral ligament, and subacromial space.

Ronald P. Pfeiffer and Brent C. Mangus

Concepts of Athletic Training FOURTH EDITION

Biceps Tendon Problems

- Long head of the tendon can be compressed within the subacromial space (impingement syndrome).
- Long head of the tendon may develop tendinitis that can result in subluxation.
- When the tendon enlarges as a result of inflammation, it becomes less stable in the groove.
- Violent force may subluxate the long head of the tendon from the bicipital groove.

Ronald P. Pfeiffer and Brent C. Mangus
Concepts of Athletic Training *FOURTH EDITION*

Biceps Tendon Problems
(continued)

Signs and symptoms include:

- Painful abduction of the shoulder joint.
- Pain in shoulder joint when the athlete supinates the forearm against resistance.
- Resisted flexion and supination yields a snapping and/or popping sensation.

Ronald P. Pfeiffer and Brent C. Mangus
Concepts of Athletic Training *FOURTH EDITION*

Biceps Tendon Problems
(continued)

First Aid

- This is an "overuse" type of injury; there are no first aid procedures for the chronic condition.
- Traumatic subluxations should be treated with immediate application of ice and compression.
- Long-term care includes rest, anti-inflammatories, and gradually progressive rehabilitation exercises.
- If symptoms persist, surgery may be necessary.

Ronald P. Pfeiffer and Brent C. Mangus
Concepts of Athletic Training *FOURTH EDITION*

Contusions of the Shoulder
Region

- In sports, external blows are common to this region.
- The GH joint is well protected by muscles while the AC joint is exposed.
- Contusions to this region can result in a "shoulder pointer."

Notes

_____

_____

_____

_____

_____

_____

_____

_____

_____

_____

_____

Ronald P. Pfeiffer and Brent C. Mangus

Concepts of Athletic Training FOURTH EDITION

Contusions of the Shoulder Region (continued)

Signs and symptoms include:

- Recent history of blow to shoulder.
- Decreased ROM.
- Muscle spasm.
- Discoloration & swelling, especially over bony areas such as the AC joint.

First Aid

- Immediate application of ice and compression.

- Sling & swathe bandage.

- If significant swelling persists for more than 72 hours, refer athlete to physician.

Chapter 12: Injuries to the Arm, Wrist, and Hand

Notes

_____

Concepts of Athletic Training FOURTH EDITION
Ronald P. Pfeiffer
Brent C. Mangus

Chapter 12

Injuries to the Arm, Wrist, and Hand

Ronald P. Pfeiffer and Brent C. Mangus
Concepts of Athletic Training FOURTH EDITION

Anatomy Review

- The bones of the arm are the humerus, radius, and ulna.
- The elbow is comprised of three articulations, the humeroulnar, humeroradial, and proximal radioulnar joints.
- Distal end of the forearm articulates with carpal bones to form the radiocarpal and distal radioulnar joints.

Ronald P. Pfeiffer and Brent C. Mangus
Concepts of Athletic Training FOURTH EDITION

Anatomy Review (continued)

- Joints of the arm allow flexion/extension and pronation/supination at the elbow.

- Joints of the wrist allow flexion/extension and radial & ulnar deviation.

Notes

_____

_____

_____

_____

_____

_____

_____

_____

_____

_____

_____

_____

_____

_____

_____

_____

_____

_____

_____

_____

_____

_____

_____

_____

_____

_____

_____

_____

_____

_____

_____

_____

_____

_____

_____

_____

_____

_____

_____

_____

_____

_____

_____

_____

_____

Ronald P. Pfeiffer and Brent C. Mangus

Concepts of Athletic Training FOURTH EDITION

Anatomy Review (continued)

Annular ligament stabilizes the head of the radius with the radioulnar joint.

Ronald P. Pfeiffer and Brent C. Mangus

Concepts of Athletic Training FOURTH EDITION

Anatomy Review (continued)

Ronald P. Pfeiffer and Brent C. Mangus

Concepts of Athletic Training FOURTH EDITION

Anatomy Review (continued)

Notes

_____
_____
_____
_____
_____
_____
_____
_____
_____
_____
_____
_____
_____
_____
_____
_____
_____
_____
_____
_____
_____
_____
_____
_____
_____
_____
_____
_____
_____
_____
_____
_____

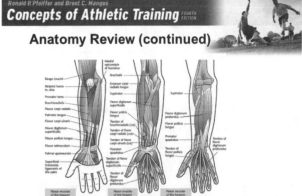

Anatomy Review (continued)

Soft Tissue Injuries to the Upper Arm

Contusions and Fractures

- Such injuries are common in contact sports.
- Muscle tissue is compressed between skin and bone.
- Significance of damage is directly proportional to the force involved.
- Repeated episodes can result in myositis ossificans traumatica.

Soft Injuries to the Upper Arm (continued)

Myositis Ossificans Traumatica

- Chronic inflammation of the muscle that results in the development of bone-like tissue within the muscle.
- May cause exostosis, a "benign growth projecting from a bone surface capped by cartilage."

Myositis ossificans traumatica develops over weeks or months and is often ignored during the early stages.

Notes

_____

_____

_____

_____

_____

_____

_____

_____

_____

_____

_____

_____

_____

_____

_____

_____

_____

_____

_____

_____

_____

_____

_____

_____

_____

_____

_____

_____

_____

_____

_____

_____

_____

_____

_____

_____

Ronald P. Pfeiffer and Brent C. Mangus
Concepts of Athletic Training FOURTH EDITION

Myositis Ossificans Traumatica (continued)

Signs and symptoms include:

- Recent history of contusion.
- Pain, discoloration, and swelling.
- Muscle spasm and strength loss.
- Loss of sensation distally.

First Aid

- Apply ice and compression.
- Place arm in a sling.
- If symptoms persist for 72 hours, refer to a physician.

Ronald P. Pfeiffer and Brent C. Mangus
Concepts of Athletic Training FOURTH EDITION

Triceps Injuries

Triceps injuries are uncommon in sports.

- Mechanism is a direct blow or fall on outstretched hand.
- Either mechanism can result in partial or complete rupture of muscle or tendon.

Injury may occur in a wide variety of sports, including:

- Competitive weight lifting.
- Power lifting.
- Body building.
- Alpine skiing.
- Volleyball.

Ronald P. Pfeiffer and Brent C. Mangus
Concepts of Athletic Training FOURTH EDITION

Triceps Injuries (continued)

Signs and symptoms include:

- History of sudden popping in posterior humerus or elbow region.
- Pain in elbow region or just proximal in the area of triceps tendon.
- Visible defect within muscle or tendon near olecranon process.
- Discoloration and swelling.

First Aid

- Immediate application of ice and compression.
- Placement of arm in a sling with elbow flexed to 90°, if pain is tolerated.
- Referral to a physician.

Notes

Ronald P. Pfeiffer and Brent C. Mangus
Concepts of Athletic Training FOURTH EDITION

Fractures of the Upper Arm

Although rare, such fractures may be associated with activities that involve collisions between participants or high speed falls.

Signs and symptoms include:

- Severe pain in upper arm.
- Deformity & loss of function and unwillingness to use arm.
- Muscle spasm.
- Athlete reports an audible snap or pop at the time of injury.
- Sensory loss in forearm, if radial nerve is affected.

Ronald P. Pfeiffer and Brent C. Mangus
Concepts of Athletic Training FOURTH EDITION

Fractures of the Upper Arm (continued)

First aid includes:

- Immediate application of ice and compression.
- Properly constructed splint.
- Discontinuing ice if symptoms indicate radial nerve involvement or circulatory deficit is developing.
- Sling-and-swathe bandage.
- Treatment for shock and transport immediately to medical facility.

Ronald P. Pfeiffer and Brent C. Mangus
Concepts of Athletic Training FOURTH EDITION

Elbow Injuries

Sprains and Dislocations

- The three joints that comprise the elbow are bound together by several ligaments.
- Ulnar & radial collateral ligaments protect elbow from valgus and varus forces.
- Injury mechanism includes falling backwards with elbow locked in extension.
- Sprains also result from both valgus and varus forces that occur as the arm is trapped in a vulnerable position.
- Elbow dislocations constitute extreme sprains.

Notes

Concepts of Athletic Training FOURTH EDITION
Ronald P. Pfeiffer and Brent C. Mangus

Elbow Dislocations (continued)

Mechanism for this injury includes falling either on a flexed or fully extended arm. The deformity is usually obvious.

Humerus
Olecranon process
Radius
Ulna

Concepts of Athletic Training FOURTH EDITION
Ronald P. Pfeiffer and Brent C. Mangus

Elbow Dislocation (continued)

Signs and symptoms include:

- Mild swelling & localized pain in minor sprains.
- Difficulty in gripping or making a fist.
- Gross elbow deformity in dislocations.
- Loss of function & severe pain.
- Possible neurological symptoms.

Concepts of Athletic Training FOURTH EDITION
Ronald P. Pfeiffer and Brent C. Mangus

Elbow Dislocation (continued)

First aid includes:

- Application of ice & compression.
- Application of splint & sling-and-swathe bandage.
- Monitoring distal pulse.
- Treatment for shock.
- Summon EMS.

Notes

_____
_____
_____
_____
_____
_____
_____
_____
_____
_____
_____
_____
_____
_____
_____
_____
_____
_____
_____
_____
_____
_____
_____
_____
_____
_____
_____
_____
_____
_____
_____
_____
_____
_____
_____
_____
_____

Ronald P. Pfeiffer and Brent C. Mangus
Concepts of Athletic Training FOURTH EDITION

Elbow Fractures

- Elbow fractures generally involve the distal humerus or the proximal ulna or radius.
- If radial artery is compressed, there is risk of Volkmann's contracture.
- Injury mechanism is similar to sprains and dislocations.

Ronald P. Pfeiffer and Brent C. Mangus
Concepts of Athletic Training FOURTH EDITION

Elbow Fractures (continued)

Signs and symptoms include:

- Recent history of elbow trauma.
- Significant pain and dysfunction.
- Immediate swelling.
- Deformity in cases of displaced fractures.

If forearm feels cold & clammy, and the athlete reports numbness in the hand, the forearm's blood supply is compromised.

Ronald P. Pfeiffer and Brent C. Mangus
Concepts of Athletic Training FOURTH EDITION

Elbow Fractures (continued)

First Aid

- Immediate application of ice, but **avoid compressing the joint.**
- Application of splint (avoid moving elbow bones) and support of the arm in a sling.
- Treatment for shock.
- Arrange for transport to medical facility.

Notes

Epicondylitis of the Elbow

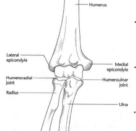

- Medial epicondyle is the attachment site of the forearm flexors and ulnar collateral ligament.

- Lateral epicondyle is the attachment site of forearm extensors and radial collateral ligaments.

- Sports that require gripping combined with wrist movements place much stress on the epicondylar region.

Epicondylitis of the Elbow (continued)

- Little League baseball pitching ("Little League elbow") and golf ("golfer's elbow") associated with medial epicondyle injury.

- Tennis elbow involves the lateral humeral epicondyle and the tendon of the extensor carpi radialis brevis muscle.

  - Factors include:
    - excessive number of strokes.
    - incorrect technique.
    - racket handle that's too small.
    - change in racket materials.
    - grip that's too tight.
    - muscle imbalance.

Epicondylitis of the Elbow (continued)

Signs and symptoms include:

- Pain and swelling in the region of one or both epicondyles.

- Pain that worsens with activity.

- Radiating pain into forearm muscles.

- Epicondylar pain associated with resisted wrist movements.

First aid is not practical, but if symptoms worsen:

- Apply ice and compression.

- Refer to physician if pain persists.

Notes

_____

_____

_____

_____

_____

_____

_____

_____

_____

_____

_____

_____

_____

_____

_____

_____

_____

_____

_____

_____

_____

_____

_____

_____

_____

_____

_____

_____

_____

_____

_____

_____

_____

_____

_____

_____

Ronald P. Pfeiffer and Brent C. Mangus
Concepts of Athletic Training FOURTH EDITION

Elbow Injuries (continued)

Osteochondritis Dissecans

- Throwing mechanism can result in impingement between radial head and capitellum of the humerus.
- High velocity elbow extension can cause abnormal compression of the joint on lateral side.
- Cartilage on proximal end of the radius becomes inflamed and may fracture, resulting in osteochondritis dissecans.
- Axial loading of forearm may also result in this condition.

Ronald P. Pfeiffer and Brent C. Mangus
Concepts of Athletic Training FOURTH EDITION

Osteochondritis Dissecans (continued)

Signs and symptoms include:
- Pain during sports participation.
- Joint inflammation and stiffness occurring 12 to 24 hrs. after participation.
- "Locking" of elbow joint.
- Osteoarthritis in advanced cases.

First Aid
- Apply ice and compression.
- Refer athlete to a physician.

Ronald P. Pfeiffer and Brent C. Mangus
Concepts of Athletic Training FOURTH EDITION

Elbow Injuries (continued)

Contusions of the Elbow

Blows to the elbow are common; the majority result in temporary symptoms.

- Exception involves the olecranon bursa.
- Repeated irritation of the bursa can result in inflammation (bursitis).

Notes

Contusions of the Elbow
(continued)

Signs and symptoms include:

- Swelling around the olecranon process.
- Pain and stiffness, especially when elbow is flexed.
- Elevated skin temperature over olecranon process, skin may be taut, and joint may show signs of internal hemorrhage.

First Aid

- Apply ice and compression.
- In cases of bursitis, refer to a physician.

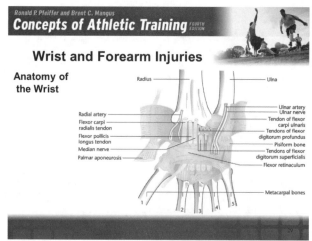

Wrist and Forearm Injuries

Anatomy of the Wrist

Wrist and Forearm Injuries
(continued)

Anatomy of the wrist

- Complex structure due to small size and large number of tendons that serve the wrist, thumb, and fingers.
- Tendons are held in place by the retinaculum.
- Major vessels and nerves pass through this region. They are:
    - Ulnar and radial arteries and veins.
    - Ulnar, median, and radial nerves.

Notes

Ronald P. Pfeiffer and Brent C. Mangus
Concepts of Athletic Training FOURTH EDITION

Wrist and Forearm Injuries (continued)

Fracture through distal radius

Distal forearm fractures are rare in sports.

- **Colles' fracture,** a transverse fracture of the distal radius, is the most serious.

Ronald P. Pfeiffer and Brent C. Mangus
Concepts of Athletic Training FOURTH EDITION

Colles' Fracture

Signs and symptoms include:

- History of significant trauma.
- Feeling the bone snap or hearing a popping sound.
- Deformity; severe swelling that may affect hand and fingers; severe pain; and significant loss of wrist, hand, or finger motion.

Loss of sensation in either hand or fingers may occur.

Ronald P. Pfeiffer and Brent C. Mangus
Concepts of Athletic Training FOURTH EDITION

Colles' Fracture (continued)

First Aid

- Immediately apply ice, compression, and elevation.
- Do not use ice if you suspect the vascular or nerve supply is affected.
- Treat for shock and transport to medical facility.

Notes

_____

_____

_____

_____

_____

_____

_____

_____

_____

_____

_____

_____

_____

_____

_____

_____

_____

_____

_____

_____

_____

_____

_____

_____

_____

_____

_____

_____

_____

_____

_____

_____

_____

Ronald P. Pfeiffer and Brent C. Mangus
Concepts of Athletic Training FOURTH EDITION
Wrist Fractures

- Fractures of carpal bones common in sports.

- Most common wrist fractures involve scaphoid bone and tend to occur at the "waist," the narrowest portion of the bone.

- Deformity is typically not present.

- When in doubt, refer to physician.

Ronald P. Pfeiffer and Brent C. Mangus
Concepts of Athletic Training FOURTH EDITION
Wrist Fractures (continued)

Signs and symptoms include:

- History of wrist trauma with popping or snapping sensation.

- Pain with movement, wrist feels locked, and a positive "snuffbox" test.

Ronald P. Pfeiffer and Brent C. Mangus
Concepts of Athletic Training FOURTH EDITION
Wrist Fractures (continued)

First Aid

- Apply I.C.E.

- Apply a splint that immobilizes wrist.

- Support with sling-and-swathe bandage, leaving fingertips exposed to monitor blood flow beyond the splint.

Notes

Wrist Sprains & Dislocations

The same mechanisms that cause fractures can also cause sprains or dislocations in the region.

- Injury affects radiocarpal (wrist) joint and ligaments.

Ligamentous Anatomy -- Palmar

Wrist Sprains & Dislocations (continued)

- Lunate bone is the most commonly dislocated bone of wrist.

- Mechanism of this injury is forceful hyperextension.

Ligamentous Anatomy -- Dorsal

Wrist Sprains & Dislocations (continued)

Signs and symptoms include:

- History of injury combined with snapping/popping sensation.
- Painful movement; movement may be impossible.
- Numbness and/or pain radiating into hands or fingers.

First Aid

- Apply I.C.E.
- Splint with sling & swathe bandage.
  - Expose fingertips.
- Refer athlete to a physician.

Notes

_____
_____
_____
_____
_____
_____
_____
_____
_____
_____
_____
_____
_____
_____
_____
_____
_____
_____
_____
_____
_____
_____
_____
_____
_____
_____
_____
_____
_____
_____
_____
_____
_____
_____
_____
_____

Ronald P. Pfeiffer and Brent C. Mangus
Concepts of Athletic Training FOURTH EDITION

Nerve Injuries to the Wrist

- Median nerve, which passes through carpal tunnel, is most commonly injured nerve in the region.
- Carpal tunnel syndrome may be related to tendonitis or sprains in the region.

- Majority of carpal tunnel syndrome cases involve overuse injuries.
- Sports requiring gripping for extended periods have high incidence.

Ronald P. Pfeiffer and Brent C. Mangus
Concepts of Athletic Training FOURTH EDITION

Nerve Injuries to the Wrist (continued)

Signs and symptoms include:

- Loss of sensation to a portion of hand and fingers and loss of strength in fingers affected by the nerve.
- Pain and tenderness on palmar side of the wrist.
- Associated tendonitis.
- Symptoms may worsen when the wrist is fully flexed or extended or an objected is gripped.

Ronald P. Pfeiffer and Brent C. Mangus
Concepts of Athletic Training FOURTH EDITION

Nerve Injuries to the Wrist (continued)

First Aid

- Since this injury tends to develop over time, first aid is not a concern.
- If the injury is associated with acute trauma, treat with I.C.E.
  - Do not apply ice if vascular or nerve supply is compromised
- Any athlete complaining of such symptoms should be referred to a physician.

Notes

_____

Ronald P. Pfeiffer and Brent C. Mangus

Concepts of Athletic Training FOURTH EDITION

Nerve Injuries to the Wrist (continued)

Extensor pollicis brevis and abductor pollicis longus
Extensor pollicis longus
Superficial radial nerve

de Quervain's Disease may be the most common form of tenosynovitis of the wrist.

Condition involves the tendons of the thumb:
- The extensor pollicis brevis and the abductor pollicis longus.
- Thumb flexion and extension will be painful.

Ronald P. Pfeiffer and Brent C. Mangus

Concepts of Athletic Training FOURTH EDITION

Nerve Injuries to the Wrist (continued)

Signs and symptoms include:
- Pain and tenderness around the radial styloid process.
- Pain and swelling in thumb tendons.
- Tendons may catch within the wrist during activity.
- Thumb flexion with ulnar deviation increases pain and related symptoms.

First Aid
- Rest, immobilization with some form of splint, and anti-inflammatory medication.
- Surgery may be necessary in advanced or recurring cases.

Ronald P. Pfeiffer and Brent C. Mangus

Concepts of Athletic Training FOURTH EDITION

Ganglions

Ganglion of the extensor tendon

Ganglion results from a herniation of the synovium surrounding a tendon.

- Herniated area becomes filled with fluid.
- Some ganglions are soft; others are hard and painful.

Injuries to the Arm, Wrist, and Hand

Notes

Concepts of Athletic Training FOURTH EDITION

Ganglions (continued)

Signs and symptoms include:

- Visible swelling.
- Painful, hardened nodule, in advanced cases.

First Aid
- Some ganglions spontaneously regress.
- Leave alone, if possible.
- They can be surgically removed.

Concepts of Athletic Training FOURTH EDITION

Hand Injuries

Phalanges

Hamate
Capitate
Triquetral
Lunate

Metacarpals
Trapezium
Trapezoid
Scaphoid

Ulna

Radius

Hand Fractures

Fractures can occur to any of the 19 bones in the hand.

Concepts of Athletic Training FOURTH EDITION

Hand Fractures (continued)

1st metacarpal

Trapezium

Tendon of abductor pollicis longus

- Bennett's fracture is unique thumb injury.
- Boxer's Fracture
  - Mechanism includes blows with a clenched fist.
  - Fracture involves 4th and/or 5th metacarpal bone(s) near the proximal end(s).
  - Metacarpals can be fractured by a crushing mechanism.
  - Phalangeal fractures are common in sports.

Notes

Ronald P. Pfeiffer and Brent C. Mangus

Concepts of Athletic Training FOURTH EDITION

Hand Fractures (continued)

Signs and symptoms include:

- History of trauma.
- Associated pain and dysfunction of hand.
- Deformity may be present.
- Broken skin (in compound fractures).
- Significant inflammation.

Ronald P. Pfeiffer and Brent C. Mangus

Concepts of Athletic Training FOURTH EDITION

Hand Fractures (continued)

First Aid

- Apply I.C.E.
- Apply splint and sling & swathe bandage.
  - Leave fingernails exposed.
  - An isolated phalangeal fracture can be buddy-taped to an adjacent finger.
- Refer athlete to a physician.

Ronald P. Pfeiffer and Brent C. Mangus

Concepts of Athletic Training FOURTH EDITION

Sprains and Dislocations of the Hand

Any joint in the hand can be involved. Most common forms are:

- Gamekeeper's thumb.
- Mallet finger.
- Boutonnière deformity.

Gamekeeper's thumb involves sprain of the ulnar collateral ligament of the thumb.
- Mechanism of injury is a valgus force to the MP joint of the thumb.
- Thumb is unstable.

Notes

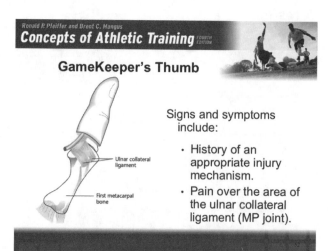

GameKeeper's Thumb

Signs and symptoms include:

- History of an appropriate injury mechanism.
- Pain over the area of the ulnar collateral ligament (MP joint).

Ulnar collateral ligament

First metacarpal bone

Concepts of Athletic Training FOURTH EDITION
Ronald P. Pfeiffer and Brent C. Mangus

GameKeeper's Thumb (continued)

Signs and symptoms include:

- Snapping or popping at the time of injury.
- Swelling of the MP joint.
- Inability to move the thumb.
- Inability to grip tightly using the thumb.

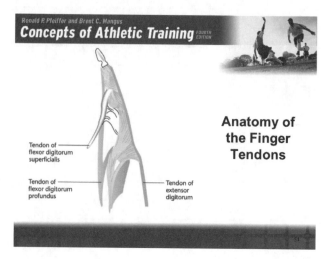

Concepts of Athletic Training FOURTH EDITION
Ronald P. Pfeiffer and Brent C. Mangus

Anatomy of the Finger Tendons

Tendon of flexor digitorum superficialis

Tendon of flexor digitorum profundus

Tendon of extensor digitorum

Notes

Concepts of Athletic Training FOURTH EDITION

Mallet (Baseball) Finger

- Injury involves distal phalanx.
- Mechanism is a blow to the fingertip while extending it from a flexed position.
- Injury often occurs in baseball.

Tendon of extensor digitorum

Flexion deformity

Concepts of Athletic Training FOURTH EDITION

Mallet (Baseball) Finger (continued)

Signs and symptoms include:

- Flexon deformity is the MOST important sign.
- Recent trauma to fingertip.
- Point tenderness on dorsal side of the base of distal phalanx.
- Inability to extend fingertip.

Concepts of Athletic Training FOURTH EDITION

Mallet (Baseball) Finger (continued)

First aid care involves:
- Immediate application of I.C.E.
- Immediate application of splint with the DIP joint extended.
   - Do not let the distal phalanx fall back into flexed position.
- Elevate arm in simple sling.
- Refer to medical care facility.

Notes

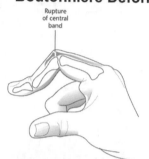

Concepts of Athletic Training
Ronald P. Pfeiffer and Brent C. Mangus

Boutonnière Deformity

Rupture
of central
band

- Injury involves proximal interphalangeal (PIP) joint. Extensor tendon is involved as it crosses the dorsal surface of the PIP.
- Mechanism of injury is a blow while the finger is flexed during active extension.

Concepts of Athletic Training
Ronald P. Pfeiffer and Brent C. Mangus

Boutonnière Deformity (continued)

Force of injury results in a tearing of the central band of the extensor digitorum tendon allowing the PIP to "pop" through the opening, like a button through a buttonhole.

Signs and symptoms include:

- History of violent flexon injury to finger.
- Significant weakness on finger extension at the PIP joint.

Concepts of Athletic Training
Ronald P. Pfeiffer and Brent C. Mangus

Boutonnière Deformity (continued)

Signs and symptoms (continued):

- Joint becomes painful, swollen, then stiff.
- If uncorrected, deformity will develop.
- Deformity is characterized by hyperextension of MP & DIP with flexion of PIP.

Notes

Ronald P. Pfeiffer and Brent C. Mangus
Concepts of Athletic Training FOURTH EDITION

Boutonnière Deformity (continued)

First Aid

- Apply I.C.E.
- Elevate in simple sling.
- Refer athlete to a physician.

Ronald P. Pfeiffer and Brent C. Mangus
Concepts of Athletic Training FOURTH EDITION

Wrist and Thumb Taping

Ronald P. Pfeiffer and Brent C. Mangus
Concepts of Athletic Training FOURTH EDITION

Wrist and Thumb Taping (continued)

Notes

Ronald P. Pfeiffer and Brent C. Mangus
Concepts of Athletic Training FOURTH EDITION

Wrist and Thumb Taping (continued)

Ronald P. Pfeiffer and Brent C. Mangus
Concepts of Athletic Training FOURTH EDITION

Wrist and Thumb Taping (continued)

Ronald P. Pfeiffer and Brent C. Mangus
Concepts of Athletic Training FOURTH EDITION

Wrist and Thumb Taping (concluded)

Chapter 13: Injuries to the Thorax and Abdomen

Notes

Concepts of
Athletic Training FOURTH EDITION
Ronald P. Pfeiffer
Brent C. Mangus

Chapter 13

Injuries to the Thorax and Abdomen

Ronald P. Pfeiffer and Brent C. Mangus
Concepts of Athletic Training FOURTH EDITION

Anatomy Review

Thoracic cage has 12 pairs of ribs.

- The first 7 pairs connect directly to sternum.
- Pairs 8 through 10 connect via common costal cartilage.
- Pairs 11 and 12 are "floating ribs."

Major thoracic joints include:

- Intervertebral.
- Sternoclavicular.
- Sternocostal.
- Costochondral.

Ronald P. Pfeiffer and Brent C. Mangus
Concepts of Athletic Training FOURTH EDITION

Anatomy Review (continued)

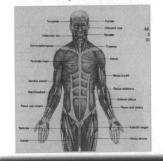

Muscles of the trunk include:

- Internal and external intercostals.
- Pectoralis major & minor.
- Rectus abdominis.
- Internal/external obliques.
- Trapezius.
- Rhomboids.
- Latissimus dorsi and others.

Notes

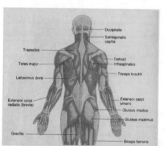

Anatomy Review (continued)

Concepts of Athletic Training FOURTH EDITION
Ronald P. Pfeiffer and Brent C. Mangus

Muscles of the trunk (posterior view)

Anatomy Review (continued)

Concepts of Athletic Training FOURTH EDITION
Ronald P. Pfeiffer and Brent C. Mangus

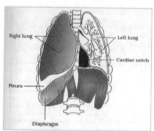

Internal thoracic organs and major blood vessels of the region are:
- Heart & pericardium.
- Lungs & pleura.
  - Thoracic aorta.
  - Pulmonary artery & veins.
  - Vena cava.
- Trachea & esophagus.
- Thymus gland.
- Lymph nodes.

Anatomy Review

Concepts of Athletic Training FOURTH EDITION
Ronald P. Pfeiffer and Brent C. Mangus

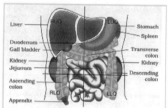

Abdominal quadrants
- RUQ
- LUQ
- RLQ
- LLQ

Notes

Anatomy Review (continued)

Abdominal Organs and Structures

RUQ contains:
- Liver, gallbladder, and right kidney.

RLQ contains:
- Appendix and ascending colon.

LUQ contains:
- Stomach, spleen, left kidney, and pancreas.

LLQ contains:
- Descending colon.

Common Sports Injuries

- Fractures can occur to ribs, sternum, clavicle, or thoracic vertebrae.
  - Injuries must be treated immediately to avoid pneumothorax or hemothorax.
- Joint dislocations and subluxations of thoracic skeletal joints can occur.
- Costochondral separations involve disunion of sternum and ribs.

Common Sports Injuries (continued)

Signs and symptoms of rib fractures include:
- Extreme localized pain that is aggravated by sneezing, coughing, and forced inhalation.
- Athlete grasps chest wall at point of injury.
- Mild swelling at site; there may be bony deformity.
- Breathing difficulties; rapid shallow breathing.

First Aid
- Monitor vital signs and watch for respiratory distress.
- Transport to medical facility.

Notes

Ronald P. Pfeiffer and Brent C. Mangus
Concepts of Athletic Training FOURTH EDITION
Common Sports Injuries (continued)

Signs and symptoms of subluxations and dislocations include:
- History of snap or popping sensations.
- Pain and tenderness over costochondral junction.
- Palpable defect may be felt, and swelling in the localized area.
- Maximum or near-maximum inhalation may be very difficult.

First Aid
- Apply ice and light compression immediately.
- Treat for shock and transport to medical facility.

Ronald P. Pfeiffer and Brent C. Mangus
Concepts of Athletic Training FOURTH EDITION
Common Sports Injuries (continued)

Breast Injuries
- Women experience contusions from direct contact in some sports.
- A sports bra does not provide protection but can provide comfort and support.
  - "Going braless" during athletic activity can stretch breast tissue resulting in loss of contour.
- Nipple irritation occurs in some athletes from shirts chafing the tissue.
  - Placing a bandage directly over the nipple during training and competition prevents irritation.
  - Changing tops may help.

Ronald P. Pfeiffer and Brent C. Mangus
Concepts of Athletic Training FOURTH EDITION
Heart Injuries

- While rare, contusions to the chest wall can bruise the heart, resulting in death.
  - Commotio cordis can occur.

- Use of AED device is the most practical way to save the lives of people experiencing commotio cordis.

Notes

Ronald P. Pfeiffer and Brent C. Mangus
Concepts of Athletic Training FOURTH EDITION

Heart Injuries (continued)

Blunt trauma to the chest can also cause aortic rupture, damage to the pericardium, or valvular damage.

- Aortic injury is often fatal and must be given immediate attention.
- Closely observe any athlete with chest injury for breathing problems, fainting, decreases in heart rate and blood pressure, and complaints of severe chest pains.

Ronald P. Pfeiffer and Brent C. Mangus
Concepts of Athletic Training FOURTH EDITION

Lung Injuries

- Pulmonary contusions may occur as complication of rib fracture, contusion, or other type of lung injury.
- Fractured rib can puncture pleural sac, causing pneumothorax.
  - Spontaneous pneumothorax can occur without trauma (reported in weight lifters and runners).
- Hemothorax occurs when fractured rib punctures lung.
  - This condition can be life threatening.

Ronald P. Pfeiffer and Brent C. Mangus
Concepts of Athletic Training FOURTH EDITION

Lung Injuries (continued)

Signs and symptoms include:

- Severe pain in chest, sometimes radiating to thoracic spine.
- Breathing problems (dyspnea).
- May have nonproductive cough and tachycardia.

Notes

Ronald P. Pfeiffer and Brent C. Mangus
Concepts of Athletic Training FOURTH EDITION

Lung Injuries (continued)

First Aid

- Treat for shock.
- Monitor vital signs.
- Transport to medical facility immediately.

Ronald P. Pfeiffer and Brent C. Mangus
Concepts of Athletic Training FOURTH EDITION

Internal Injuries to the Thorax and Abdomen

Liver, Kidneys, Spleen and Bladder Injuries

- Although fairly safe, the liver is susceptible to blunt trauma.
  - Diseases such as hepatitis make liver more vulnerable.
  - Heavy consumption of alcohol and/or use of steroids damages the liver.

Ronald P. Pfeiffer and Brent C. Mangus
Concepts of Athletic Training FOURTH EDITION

Internal Injuries to the Thorax and Abdomen (continued)

- Kidneys are susceptible to blunt trauma directed at the lower back.
- Kidneys may also be injured as a result of heat stroke
  - Be alert for hematuria.
- Refer athlete to a physician.

Notes

Ronald P. Pfeiffer and Brent C. Mangus

Concepts of Athletic Training FOURTH EDITION

Internal Injuries to the Thorax and Abdomen (continued)

The spleen is susceptible to blows in the LUQ.

- The organ serves as a reservoir for RBCs.
- It has an ability to "splint" itself when lacerated.
- Be alert for Kehr's sign.
- Athlete recovering from mononucleosis MUST be cleared by a physician to return to participation

Ronald P. Pfeiffer and Brent C. Mangus

Concepts of Athletic Training FOURTH EDITION

Internal Injuries to the Thorax and Abdomen (continued)

The bladder is not commonly injured in sports.

- A direct blow to the bladder may injure the organ.
- Signs are pain in the area and blood in urine.

To avoid injury, encourage athletes to empty their bladder prior to participation.

Chapter 14: Injuries to the Hip and Pelvis

Notes

Concepts of Athletic Training FOURTH EDITION
Ronald P. Pfeiffer
Brent C. Mangus

Chapter 14

Injuries to the Hip and Pelvis

Ronald P. Pfeiffer and Brent C. Mangus
Concepts of Athletic Training FOURTH EDITION

Anatomy Review

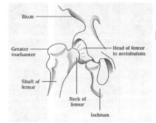

Primary Hip Structures
- Ilium
- Ischium
- Pubis
- Innominate bone

Ronald P. Pfeiffer and Brent C. Mangus
Concepts of Athletic Training FOURTH EDITION

Anatomy Review (continued)

Functions of the pelvis include:
- Attachment of lower extremities.
- Protection of internal organs.
- Muscle attachments.
- Birth process, in females.

Joints (other than hip)
- Sacroiliac
- Pubic symphysis

Notes

_____
_____
_____
_____
_____
_____
_____
_____
_____
_____
_____
_____
_____
_____
_____
_____
_____
_____
_____
_____
_____
_____
_____
_____
_____
_____
_____
_____
_____
_____
_____
_____
_____
_____

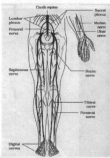

Concepts of Athletic Training — FOURTH EDITION
Ronald P. Pfeiffer and Brent C. Mangus

Anatomy Review (continued)

Major Nerves
- Femoral
- Sciatic
- Obturator (not shown)
- Saphenous
- Tibial
- Peroneal
- Plantar nerves (not shown)
- Digital nerves

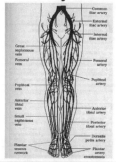

Concepts of Athletic Training — FOURTH EDITION
Ronald P. Pfeiffer and Brent C. Mangus

Anatomy Review (continued)

Major Vessels
- External iliac
- Femoral
- Deep profunda femoral (not shown)
- Saphenous vein
- Popliteal
- Anterior tibial
- Posterior tibial
- Dorsalis pedis
- Plantar

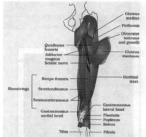

Concepts of Athletic Training — FOURTH EDITION
Ronald P. Pfeiffer and Brent C. Mangus

Anatomy Review (continued)

Posterior Muscles
- Gluteals-- maximus, medius, minimus
- Deep external rotators-- piriformis, gemelli, obturators, quadratus femoris
- Hamstrings-- biceps femoris, semitendinosus, semimembranosus

Ronald P. Pfeiffer and Brent C. Mangus

Concepts of Athletic Training FOURTH EDITION

Anatomy Review (continued)

Anterior Muscles

- Psoas major & minor
- Iliacus
- Pectineus
- Adductors -- magnus, longus, brevis

Ronald P. Pfeiffer and Brent C. Mangus

Concepts of Athletic Training FOURTH EDITION

Anatomy Review (continued)

Anterior Muscles (continued)

- Gracilis
- Tensor fascia latae
- Quadriceps -- vastus muscles, rectus femoris

Ronald P. Pfeiffer and Brent C. Mangus

Concepts of Athletic Training FOURTH EDITION

Common Sports Injuries: Skeletal Injuries

Fractures of the Pelvis

- Pelvic fractures are devastating injuries.
- Pelvic fractures are not common in sports, because it typically takes a great deal of force to fracture the pelvis.
- This injury may occur in sports such as hockey, pole-vault, or football.
- Pelvic fractures in the adolescent can be serious.

Notes

_____

_____

_____

_____

_____

_____

_____

_____

_____

_____

_____

_____

_____

_____

_____

_____

_____

_____

_____

_____

_____

_____

_____

_____

_____

_____

_____

_____

_____

_____

_____

_____

_____

_____

_____

_____

Ronald P. Pfeiffer and Brent C. Mangus
Concepts of Athletic Training FOURTH EDITION
Fractures of the Pelvis (continued)

Signs and symptoms include:

- Abnormal pain in pelvic region.
- Swelling at the injury site, usually accompanied with visual or palpable deformity.
- Pain elicited when iliac crests are pressed together.
- Injury to internal organ(s) may be associated with this injury.

Ronald P. Pfeiffer and Brent C. Mangus
Concepts of Athletic Training FOURTH EDITION
Fractures of the Pelvis (continued)

First Aid

- Treat for shock and internal bleeding.
- Monitor vital signs.
- Arrange for transportation to a medical facility on a spine board, elevated at the feet.

An athlete with suspected pelvic fracture should not be allowed to return to participation before obtaining a physician's approval.

Ronald P. Pfeiffer and Brent C. Mangus
Concepts of Athletic Training FOURTH EDITION
Adolescent Pelvic Fractures

Femoral Neck Stress Fracture

- Commonly occurs in amenorrheic athletes involved in endurance sports.
- Athlete complains of severe anterior thigh or groin pain and experiences pain when walking.

Slipped Capital Femoral Epiphysis

- Commonly occurs in prepubescent boys, particularly tall boys who experienced recent growth spurt, overweight boys, and late-maturing boys.

Notes

_____
_____
_____
_____
_____
_____
_____
_____
_____
_____
_____
_____
_____
_____
_____
_____
_____
_____
_____
_____
_____
_____
_____
_____
_____
_____
_____
_____
_____
_____

Ronald P. Pfeiffer and Brent C. Mangus
Concepts of Athletic Training FOURTH EDITION

Hip Pointer

Hip Pointer is a common injury, involving a contusion to the anterior/superior portion of the iliac crest.

- Although extremely painful and debilitating, it does not require immediate medical attention.
- Signs and symptoms include swelling, pain, and discoloration at injury site.
- Athlete may walk with slight limp.

Ronald P. Pfeiffer and Brent C. Mangus
Concepts of Athletic Training FOURTH EDITION

Hip Pointer (continued)

First Aid

- Apply ice immediately.
- Athlete should rest and avoid activities involving lower extremities.
- In severe cases, crutches may be necessary.
- Permit limited participation within 1 to 2 weeks.

Ronald P. Pfeiffer and Brent C. Mangus
Concepts of Athletic Training FOURTH EDITION

Hip Pointer (continued)

- Pad the area to avoid recurrence.

Ronald P. Pfeiffer and Brent C. Mangus
Concepts of Athletic Training FOURTH EDITION

Osteitis Pubis

- This injury results from constant stress and possibly some degeneration in the pubic symphysis joint.
- Long distance runners, basketball players, and any athlete experiencing repetitive loading of this area is vulnerable.
- Male athletes may have testicular or scrotal pain, along with discomfort in the anterior pubic, suprapubic, or hip areas.

Ronald P. Pfeiffer and Brent C. Mangus
Concepts of Athletic Training FOURTH EDITION

Osteitis Pubis (continued)

First Aid

- Refer to a physician.
- Condition often responds well to rest, ice, and over-the-counter anti-inflammatory medications.
- It may take 3 months to a year to recover.

Ronald P. Pfeiffer and Brent C. Mangus
Concepts of Athletic Training FOURTH EDITION

Hip Dislocation

Dislocated Hip

- This serious injury is rare in sports, but it may occur in contact/collision sports.
- Injury can occur from a violent collision such as seen in tackle football or ice hockey.
- The mechanism of injury: The hip is in flexion and force is applied through the femur.

Notes

_____

_____

_____

_____

_____

_____

_____

_____

_____

_____

_____

_____

_____

_____

_____

_____

_____

_____

_____

_____

_____

_____

_____

_____

_____

_____

_____

_____

_____

_____

_____

_____

_____

Ronald P. Pfeiffer and Brent C. Mangus

Concepts of Athletic Training FOURTH EDITION

Hip Dislocation (continued)

Signs and symptoms include:
- Generally posterior dislocation.
- Pain and loss of movement in affected leg.
- Swelling that is palpable.
- Knee of the involved leg is angled towards the opposite leg.

First Aid
- Treat for shock.
- Immobilize the athlete and contact EMS.
- Monitor blood flow to the leg at all times.

Ronald P. Pfeiffer and Brent C. Mangus

Concepts of Athletic Training FOURTH EDITION

Avulsion Factures of the Hip

In an avulsion fracture, a bone fragment is torn away with tendon attached.

- Avulsion fractures of the hip are uncommon but can occur -- ischial tuberosity and pubis are likely sites of this injury.
- Injury likely to occur while sprinting or jumping.

Ronald P. Pfeiffer and Brent C. Mangus

Concepts of Athletic Training FOURTH EDITION

Avulsion Fractures of the Hip (continued)

Signs and symptoms include:

- Pain and swelling at site of injury.
- Inability to use the muscle group involved due to avulsion.
- Point tenderness over injury
- Snapping or popping sensation at the time of injury.

Notes

Ronald P. Pfeiffer and Brent C. Mangus
Concepts of Athletic Training FOURTH EDITION

Avulsion Fractures of the Hip (continued)

First Aid

- Immediately apply ice.
- Have athlete rest.
- Limit athlete's movements. Crutches may be necessary for walking.
- Refer to a physician for evaluation.

Ronald P. Pfeiffer and Brent C. Mangus
Concepts of Athletic Training FOURTH EDITION

Injuries to Male Genitalia

These injuries are usually transient in nature.

- Scrotal trauma can cause testicular contusion.

- Severe trauma can rupture testicle.

Wearing a protective cup is advised in collision/contact sports.

Ronald P. Pfeiffer and Brent C. Mangus
Concepts of Athletic Training FOURTH EDITION

Testicular or Scrotal Contusions

Signs and symptoms include:

- Extreme pain & point tenderness.
- Assuming fetal position and grasping testicles.
- Athlete's report of a blow to the testicles.

First Aid

- Apply ice, and allow athlete to rest, lying down.
- In cases of swelling or pain lasting longer than a few minutes, refer to a physician.
- Testicular torsion can occur and results in considerable discomfort. Transport to medical care facility.

Hernias

A hernia is a protrusion of viscera through abdominal wall.

- Inguinal hernia is more common in males
- Femoral hernia is more common in females.
- Athlete should seek the advice of a physician regarding surgical options.
- In a sports hernia, the posterior inguinal wall is weakened without protrusion of abdominal contents. No palpable hernia is detected, but athlete complains of pain in groin and lower abdominal areas.

Nerve Problems

A common complaint is burning or tingling sensation radiating from the hip to buttocks area and going down the leg.

- This discomfort often results from sciatic nerve irritation.
- Continuing to participate in the activity aggravates the irritation.
- Refer athlete to a physician.
- Rest, stretching, and strengthening exercises may be helpful.

Chapter 15: Injuries to the Thigh, Leg, and Knee

Notes

**Concepts of
Athletic Training** FOURTH EDITION
Ronald P. Pfeiffer
Brent C. Mangus

Chapter 15

Injuries to the Thigh, Leg, and Knee

Ronald P. Pfeiffer and Brent C. Mangus
Concepts of Athletic Training FOURTH EDITION

Anatomy Review

Bones of the Region

Femur

Patella

Tibia

Fibula

Ronald P. Pfeiffer and Brent C. Mangus
Concepts of Athletic Training FOURTH EDITION

Anatomy Review (continued)

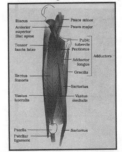

Muscles of the Region

- Quadriceps
- Hamstrings
- Abductors
- Adductors

Notes

Ronald P. Pfeiffer and Brent C. Mangus

Concepts of Athletic Training FOURTH EDITION

Anatomy Review (continued)

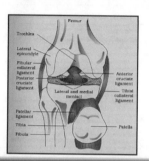

Knee Ligaments

Major ligaments are:

- Ttibial or medial collateral.
- Fibular or lateral collateral.
- Anterior cruciate.
- Posterior cruciate.

Medial and lateral collaterals protect the knee from valgus/varus forces.

Ronald P. Pfeiffer and Brent C. Mangus

Concepts of Athletic Training FOURTH EDITION

Common Sports Injuries

Fractures of the Femur and/or Patella

- Femoral fractures result from an extremely traumatic event.
- These injuries may also be in the form of a stress fracture, especially in the femoral neck region.
- Patellar fractures almost always occur as a result of a traumatic event

---

Ronald P. Pfeiffer and Brent C. Mangus

Concepts of Athletic Training FOURTH EDITION

Fractures of the Femur and/or Patella

- In the adolescent, femoral fractures include slipped capital epiphysis type.
- In the adult, fractures of the femoral neck may result in avascular necrosis of the femoral head.
  - This injury results from disrupted blood supply to the articular cartilage on the femoral head.

Notes

Ronald P. Pfeiffer and Brent C. Mangus
Concepts of Athletic Training FOURTH EDITION

Fractures of the Femur and/or Patella (continued)

Signs and symptoms include:

- Pain at the injury site.
- Difficulty walking on the affected leg.
- Swelling and/or deformity. Athlete's report of having suffered a traumatic event.
- Athlete may report a pop or snap at time of injury.

The injury needs to be evaluated by a physician. Avascular necrosis is a serious complication.

Ronald P. Pfeiffer and Brent C. Mangus
Concepts of Athletic Training FOURTH EDITION

Fractures of the Femur and/or Patella (continued)

First Aid

- Treat for shock.
- Splint the injured leg, preferably with traction splint.
- Apply sterile dressings to any open wounds.
- Monitor vital signs and circulation to lower leg.
- Arrange for transport to a nearby medical facility.

Ronald P. Pfeiffer and Brent C. Mangus
Concepts of Athletic Training FOURTH EDITION

Dislocation of the Knee or Tibiofemoral Joint

Dislocation of the knee or the tibiofemoral joint can compromise blood flow to the lower leg.

Signs and symptoms include:

- Extreme pain.
- Dislocation of the joint.

First Aid

- The injury must be splinted.
- Refer athlete to the nearest medical facility.

Injuries to the Thigh, Leg, and Knee

Notes

_____

_____

_____

_____

_____

_____

_____

_____

_____

_____

_____

_____

_____

_____

_____

_____

_____

_____

_____

_____

_____

_____

_____

_____

_____

_____

_____

_____

_____

_____

_____

_____

_____

_____

_____

Ronald P. Pfeiffer and Brent C. Mangus
Concepts of Athletic Training FOURTH EDITION

Soft Tissue Injuries to the Thigh

- These injuries usually result from direct contact with an opponent or self-inflicted muscle strain.
- **Myositis ossificans traumatica** may develop.

Signs and symptoms of a muscle contusion include:
- History of forceful impact to the area and a feeling of tightness.
- Swelling may occur in affected area.
- Inability to forcibly contract the muscle.
- Difficulty walking with affected leg.

Ronald P. Pfeiffer and Brent C. Mangus
Concepts of Athletic Training FOURTH EDITION

Muscular Strains to the Thigh

Hamstrings and adductor muscles are most likely to sustain strains.

- Strains to adductor muscles are called "groin pulls."
- Hamstrings usually are weaker and more susceptible to strains than quadriceps.
- Groin injuries take a long time to heal. Stretching is a part of recovery program.

Ronald P. Pfeiffer and Brent C. Mangus
Concepts of Athletic Training FOURTH EDITION

Muscular Strains to the Thigh (continued)

Signs and symptoms include:
- A sharp pain in the affected muscle.
- Swelling and redness in the immediate area.
- Muscle weakness.
- Inability to contract the muscle forcibly.
- Discoloration of the area.
- A defect is visible in severe cases.

Notes

_____

_____

_____

_____

_____

_____

_____

_____

_____

_____

_____

_____

_____

_____

_____

_____

_____

_____

_____

_____

_____

_____

_____

_____

_____

_____

_____

_____

_____

_____

_____

_____

_____

_____

_____

Ronald P. Pfeiffer and Brent C. Mangus
Concepts of Athletic Training FOURTH EDITION

Muscular Strains to the Thigh (continued)

First Aid

- Apply ice and compression.
- Athlete should rest and if necessary, use crutches.
- Obtain a medical evaluation of the injury.

Ronald P. Pfeiffer and Brent C. Mangus
Concepts of Athletic Training FOURTH EDITION

Patellofemoral Joint Injuries

Acute and chronic injuries can affect patellofemoral joint. Such injuries can be debilitating and must be treated.

Osteochondritis dissecans (OCD) or "joint mice"
- Condition occurs when small pieces of bone are dislodged from joint and float within capsule.
- A bone fragment can lock a joint.
- Damage to joint surface can occur.

Ronald P. Pfeiffer and Brent C. Mangus
Concepts of Athletic Training FOURTH EDITION

Patellofemoral Joint Injuries (continued)

Signs and symptoms of OCD include:
- Chronic knee pain with exertion.
- Chronic swelling.
- Knee may lock; quadriceps may atrophy.
- One or more femoral condyles may be tender when palpated.

First Aid
- Application of ice and compression.
- If necessary, crutches for walking.
- Refer athlete to physician.

Notes

_____

_____

_____

_____

_____

_____

_____

_____

_____

_____

_____

_____

_____

_____

_____

_____

_____

_____

_____

_____

_____

_____

_____

_____

_____

_____

_____

_____

_____

_____

_____

_____

_____

_____

_____

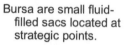

Concepts of Athletic Training
Ronald P. Pfeiffer and Brent C. Mangus

Bursa of the Knee

Bursa are small fluid-filled sacs located at strategic points.

- Numerous bursa are in the knee region; only a few are typically injured.

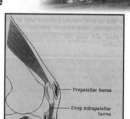

Concepts of Athletic Training
Ronald P. Pfeiffer and Brent C. Mangus

Bursa of the Knee (continued)

Inflammation can be caused by:

- Trauma.
- Infection.
- Overuse.

The prepatellar bursa is susceptible to direct trauma.

Concepts of Athletic Training
Ronald P. Pfeiffer and Brent C. Mangus

Bursa of the Knee (continued)

Signs and symptoms include:

- Swelling and tenderness at site.
- Pain when increased external pressure is applied.
- Athlete may report direct trauma to knee.

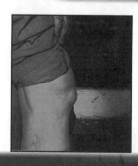

Notes

Ronald P. Pfeiffer and Brent C. Mangus

Concepts of Athletic Training FOURTH EDITION

Bursa of the Knee (continued)

First Aid

- Application of ice and compression.
- Reduced activity for a short time.
- In chronic cases, anti-inflammatory agents may be helpful.

Ronald P. Pfeiffer and Brent C. Mangus

Concepts of Athletic Training FOURTH EDITION

Patellar Dislocation/Subluxation

- Injury may be caused by a quick cutting motion that generates a great deal of abnormal force within the knee.

- Instead of moving normally, the patella moves laterally and may dislocate.

Ronald P. Pfeiffer and Brent C. Mangus

Concepts of Athletic Training FOURTH EDITION

Patellar Dislocation/Subluxation (Continued)

Signs and symptoms include:

- Severe pain and abnormal movement of the patella when injury occurred.
- Swelling.
- Patella may be obviously out-of-place.
- Extreme pain along the medial aspect of the patella.

Notes

Concepts of Athletic Training FOURTH EDITION

Patellar Dislocation/Subluxation (continued)

First Aid

- Apply ice and compression.
- Elevate.
- Splint the entire leg.
- Transport to a medical facility.

Concepts of Athletic Training FOURTH EDITION

Osgood-Schlatter Disease (OSD) and Jumper's Knee

OSD and "jumper's knee" usually involve irritation of the patellar tendon complex.

Signs and symptoms of OSD include:
- Pain and tenderness about the patellar tendon complex.
- Swelling in the area.
- Decreased ability to use the quadriceps.
- If inflammation continues, area over tibial tuberosity may become solid when palpated.

Concepts of Athletic Training FOURTH EDITION

Osgood-Schlatter Disease (OSD)

First Aid

- Apply ice and compression.
- Refer to physician for specific diagnosis.
- Until inflammation subsides, rest is important.

Ronald P. Pfeiffer and Brent C. Mangus
Concepts of Athletic Training FOURTH EDITION

Jumper's Knee

Signs and symptoms of Jumper's knee (JK) include:

- Pain and tenderness around the patellar tendon complex that may spread to tibial tuberosity.
- Decreased ability to use quadriceps for running or jumping.
- Symptoms that worsen with activity.

First Aid
- Apply ice and compression.
- Refer to physician for possible anti-inflammatory medications
- Rest will be helpful.

Ronald P. Pfeiffer and Brent C. Mangus
Concepts of Athletic Training FOURTH EDITION

Patellofemoral Conditions

Some conditions of the patella may be related to the **Q angle**.

- The Q angle is the difference between a straight line drawn from the anterior superior iliac spine and the center of the patella and a line drawn from the center of the patella through the center of the tibial tuberosity.
- An angle of 15° to 20° is acceptable.
- An excessive Q angle may be related to problems such as patellar chondromalcia.

Ronald P. Pfeiffer and Brent C. Mangus
Concepts of Athletic Training FOURTH EDITION

Menisci Injuries

Menisci are typically damaged by quick, sharp, cutting movements.

- Injury is more likely to occur if the foot is planted firmly on the playing surface.

There are many different types of tears, and they affect each athlete differently.

- In some cases, a torn flap of meniscus will get caught in the joint, causing it to lock.

Notes

_____

_____

_____

_____

_____

_____

_____

_____

_____

_____

_____

_____

_____

_____

_____

_____

_____

_____

_____

_____

_____

_____

_____

_____

_____

_____

_____

_____

_____

_____

_____

_____

Ronald P. Pfeiffer and Brent C. Mangus

Concepts of Athletic Training FOURTH EDITION

Menisci Injuries (continued)

Signs and symptoms include:

- Pop or snap when the knee was injured.
- May not see any significant swelling.
- May not be painful.
- Loss of ROM.
- Athlete may be able to continue participating.
- A feeling the knee is "giving out" periodically.

Ronald P. Pfeiffer and Brent C. Mangus

Concepts of Athletic Training FOURTH EDITION

Menisci Injuries (continued)

First Aid

- Apply ice and compression.

- Have athlete use crutches.

- Refer athlete to a physician.

Ronald P. Pfeiffer and Brent C. Mangus

Concepts of Athletic Training FOURTH EDITION

Knee Ligament Injuries

The most commonly injured knee ligaments are the MCL, LCL, and the ACL and PCL.

Common mechanisms include cutting maneuvers when running and direct blows to the joint.

Notes

[handwritten notes:] Females more common

- anatomy, Q angle,
use of muscles, hormones

Knee Ligament Injuries (continued)

Sprain to MCL is common sports injury.

- Occurs as a result of valgus stress.

- Varus stress can cause a sprain of the LCL.

Both types of sprains render knee unstable in side-to side movements.

Knee Ligament Injuries (continued)

Cruciate Ligament Injuries

- ACL can be injured when the tibia moves forcefully in an anterior direction or when the femur gets pushed backward while the tibia is held in place.
- Quick rotational movements can also damage ACL.
- The stronger the activation during eccentric contraction, the greater the likelihood of ACL injury, especially in female athletes.

Cruciate Ligament Injuries (continued)

Signs and symptoms include:

- Athlete reports the knee was forced beyond its normal ROM.
- Pain at the site of the injury.
- Swelling around the knee.
- Athlete indicates the knee feels unstable.
- Athlete reports having a snapping or popping sensation at the time of injury.

Injuries to the Thigh, Leg, and Knee

147

Notes

_____

_____

_____

_____

_____

_____

_____

_____

_____

_____

_____

_____

_____

_____

_____

_____

_____

_____

_____

_____

_____

_____

_____

_____

_____

_____

_____

_____

_____

_____

_____

_____

_____

Ronald P. Pfeiffer and Brent C. Mangus
Concepts of Athletic Training FOURTH EDITION

Cruciate Ligament Injuries (continued)

First Aid

- Immediately apply ice and compression.

- Have athlete walk on crutches.

- Refer to a physician for medical evaluation.

Ronald P. Pfeiffer and Brent C. Mangus
Concepts of Athletic Training FOURTH EDITION

Knee Bracing

Prophylactic Braces

The general consensus regarding prophylactic knee braces indicates that they do not prevent knee ligament injuries.

Prophylactic knee brace

Ronald P. Pfeiffer and Brent C. Mangus
Concepts of Athletic Training FOURTH EDITION

Knee Bracing (continued)

Functional Knee Braces

- These braces tend to work better than prophylactic braces for assisting athletes after reconstructive knee surgery.

- Monitor athletes to make sure they wear braces during participation.

- Athletes should continue wearing braces until released by a physician.

Notes

Concepts of
Athletic Training FOURTH EDITION
Ronald P. Pfeiffer
Brent C. Mangus

Chapter 16

Injuries to the Lower Leg,
Ankle, and Foot

Ronald P. Pfeiffer and Brent C. Mangus
Concepts of Athletic Training FOURTH EDITION

Anatomy Review

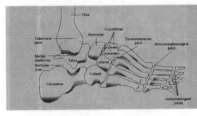

Bones and
Ligaments of the
Ankle and Foot

- Tibia
- Fibula
- Tarsals
- Metatarsals
- Phalanges

Note the subtalar joint that's responsible for
inversion and eversion of the foot

Ronald P. Pfeiffer and Brent C. Mangus
Concepts of Athletic Training FOURTH EDITION

Anatomy Review (continued)

Foot Bones (medial view)

- Tarsals
- Metatarsals

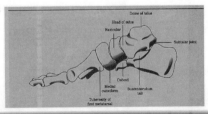

Notes

Concepts of Athletic Training FOURTH EDITION

Anatomy Review (continued)

The deltoid ligament is the primary stabilizer of the medial side of the talocrural (ankle) joint.

Concepts of Athletic Training FOURTH EDITION

Anatomy Review (continued)

Ligaments of the Ankle
(lateral view)

The three primary ligaments are:

- Anterior talofibular.
- Posterior talofibular.
- Calcaneofibular.

Concepts of Athletic Training FOURTH EDITION

Anatomy Review (continued)

- These ligaments are NOT as large or strong as the deltoid.
- Additional lateral stability is provided by the length of the fibula on the lateral side of the ankle.
- The talocrural joint is strongest in dorsiflexion and weakest in plantar flexion.

Notes

Anatomy Review (continued)

The innervation of the three compartments is supplied by the tibial, superficial, and deep peroneal nerves.

The illustration shows the anterior, lateral, and posterior leg compartments.

Common Sports Injuries

Fractures

- Most often caused by direct trauma through contact. Contact causes most fractures to the lower leg and foot.
- Repeated microtrauma can result in a stress fracture.
- Avulsion fracture of 5th metatarsal can occur with a lateral ankle sprain.

Fractures (continued)

Signs and symptoms include:

- Swelling and/or deformity at the site of fracture.
- Discoloration at the site.
- Possible broken bone end projecting through skin.
- Athlete reports a snap or pop was heard or felt.
- Inability to bear weight on the affected leg.

If the stress fracture or growth plate fracture did not result from traumatic event, the athlete complains of extreme point tenderness and pain at the site of injury.

Ronald P. Pfeiffer and Brent C. Mangus
Concepts of Athletic Training FOURTH EDITION

Fractures (continued)

First Aid

- Watch and treat for shock, if necessary.
- Apply sterile dressing to any open wounds.
- Carefully immobilize the foot and leg using a splint.
- Arrange for transport to a medical facility.

Ronald P. Pfeiffer and Brent C. Mangus
Concepts of Athletic Training FOURTH EDITION

Soft Tissue Injuries

Ankle Injuries

Ankle sprains are one of the most common injuries to this region.

- Lateral sprains are more common; 80% to 85% of all ankle sprains are to the lateral ligaments (inversion sprains).
- Eversion sprains, while less frequent, are often severe.

Ronald P. Pfeiffer and Brent C. Mangus
Concepts of Athletic Training FOURTH EDITION

Ankle Injuries: Sprains

Signs and symptoms depend on degree of sprain.

- 1st degree: Pain, mild disability, point tenderness, little laxity, little or no swelling

- 2nd degree: Pain, mild to moderate disability, point tenderness, loss of function, some laxity, swelling (mild to moderate)

- 3rd degree: Pain and severe disability, point tenderness, loss of function, laxity, moderate to severe swelling

Notes

___

Ronald P. Pfeiffer and Brent C. Mangus
Concepts of Athletic Training FOURTH EDITION

Ankle Injuries: Sprains (continued)

First Aid

- Apply ice and compression.
- Elevate.
- Apply a horseshoe- or doughnut-shaped pad.

Ronald P. Pfeiffer and Brent C. Mangus
Concepts of Athletic Training FOURTH EDITION

Ankle Injuries: Sprains (continued)

First Aid (continued)

- Have athlete use crutches with three- or four-point gait if a second- or third-degree sprain has occurred.
- If there is any question regarding the severity of the sprain, refer athlete to a medical facility for physician's evaluation.

Ronald P. Pfeiffer and Brent C. Mangus
Concepts of Athletic Training FOURTH EDITION

Ankle Injuries: Sprains (continued)

Tib-Fib Sprains

- These injuries are often treated inappropriately as lateral ankle sprains, hindering recovery.
- The difference is the mechanism of injury. Tib-fib sprains involve dorsiflexion followed by axial loading with external rotation of the foot.
- Symptoms include a positive sprain test, but athlete is also in great pain. "Squeeze test" elicits pain in syndesmosis area.

Notes

Concepts of Athletic Training FOURTH EDITION

Ankle Injuries: Sprains (continued)

First Aid

- Immediately apply ice and compression, and elevate the leg.
- Apply a doughnut shaped pad kept in place with an elastic bandage to provide compression.
- Have athlete rest and use crutches for first 72 hours, followed by wearing a walking boot for 3 to 7 days.

Ronald P. Pfeiffer and Brent C. Mangus

Concepts of Athletic Training FOURTH EDITION

Preventing Ankle Injuries

- Taping or bracing will reduce the number of ankle injuries.
- Prophylactic adhesive taping supports the ankle only for a short time.
- Bracing may be better than taping.
- Bracing combined with some high-top shoes may be helpful.

Ronald P. Pfeiffer and Brent C. Mangus

Concepts of Athletic Training FOURTH EDITION

Tendon-Related Injuries

Achilles tendon is commonly injured by long-distance runners, basketball players, and tennis players.

- Onset of tendonitis may be slow among runners, but more rapid among basketball and tennis players.
- Athletes who dramatically increase workout times or running distances, or who run on hard, uneven, or uphill surfaces are prone to Achilles tendonitis.

The injury can be either acute or chronic. Acute injuries often associated with explosive jumping or blunt trauma.

Notes

_____
_____
_____
_____
_____
_____
_____
_____
_____
_____
_____
_____
_____
_____
_____
_____
_____
_____
_____
_____
_____
_____
_____
_____
_____
_____
_____
_____
_____
_____
_____
_____
_____
_____
_____

Ronald P. Pfeiffer and Brent C. Mangus
Concepts of Athletic Training FOURTH EDITION

Achilles Tendon Injuries

Signs and symptoms include:
- Swelling and deformity at site of injury.
- Athlete reports a pop or snap associated with the injury.
- Pain in lower leg that ranges from mild to extreme.
- Loss of function, mainly in plantar flexion.

First Aid
- Immediately apply ice and compression.
- Immobilize with air cast or splint.
- Arrange for transport to nearest medical facility.

Ronald P. Pfeiffer and Brent C. Mangus
Concepts of Athletic Training FOURTH EDITION

Compartment Syndrome

Compartment syndrome usually involves the anterior compartment of the lower leg.

Chronic form is related to overuse of the compartment's muscles that causes swelling of tissues.
- Trauma, such as being kicked in the leg, can result in swelling within the compartment as well.
- In either case, swelling puts pressure on vessels and nerves.
- Properly-sized shin guards can protect lower leg.

Ronald P. Pfeiffer and Brent C. Mangus
Concepts of Athletic Training FOURTH EDITION

Compartment Syndrome (continued)

Signs and symptoms include:
- Pain and swelling in the lower leg.
- Athlete may complain of chronic or acute injury to the area.
- There may be loss of sensation or motor control to the lower leg and/or foot.
- There can be loss of pulse in the foot.
- Inability to extend the big toe or dorsiflex the foot.

First Aid
- Apply ice and elevate. Do NOT apply compression.
- If there is numbness, loss of movement, or loss of pulse to the foot, seek medical advice immediately, this is a true medical emergency.

Notes

Concepts of Athletic Training FOURTH EDITION

Shin Splints

- "Shin splints" is a very common disorder or lower leg. Term describes exercise-induced leg pain.
- The types of activities that produce this problem and the manifestations of the injury vary depending on the athlete.
- The etiology and pathology of this disorder are unclear.

Concepts of Athletic Training FOURTH EDITION

Shin Splints (continued)

Signs and symptoms include:
- Lower leg pain either medially or posteromedially.
- Typically, the athlete reports a chronic problem that progressively worsens.
- Pain can be unilateral or bilateral.

First Aid
- Apply ice and have the athlete rest.
- Use of NSAIDs may be helpful.
- Athlete may need to have his or her gait analyzed for biomechanical deficiencies.
- If problem worsens, athlete should seek medical advice.

Concepts of Athletic Training FOURTH EDITION

Plantar Fasciitis

The plantar fascia is a dense collection of tissues that traverses from the plantar aspect of the metatarsal heads to the calcaneal tuberosity.

- If this tissue becomes tight or inflamed by overuse or trauma, it can produce pain and disability.
- Typical symptom is extreme pain in the plantar aspect of the foot with the first steps taken after getting out of bed in the morning. Pain eases with following steps.
- Athlete also has point tenderness in the region of the calcaneal tuberosity.

Notes

Ronald P. Pfeiffer and Brent C. Mangus

Concepts of Athletic Training FOURTH EDITION

Plantar Fasciitis (continued)

Treatment is typically conservative and includes:

- Rest.
- Anti-inflammatories.
- Applying cold and heat alternatively to enhance healing.
- A heel pad and stretching the Achilles tendon complex can assist in recovery.
- Use of semirigid orthoses is also effective, but some athletes find it difficult to participate with such an orthotic in their shoes.

Aggravating the injury increases the healing time.

Ronald P. Pfeiffer and Brent C. Mangus

Concepts of Athletic Training FOURTH EDITION

Heel Spurs

- Heel spurs can be related to chronic plantar fasciitis.
- Chronic inflammation can result in ossification at the site of attachment on the plantar aspect of the calcaneus.
- Heel spurs result in long-term disability for many athletes.

Treatment of Heel Spurs

- Athlete should consult a physician if spurs become incapacitating.
- Applying a doughnut-shaped pad beneath the heel spur may help but rarely do they ameliorate the problem.

Ronald P. Pfeiffer and Brent C. Mangus

Concepts of Athletic Training FOURTH EDITION

Morton's Foot

Morton's foot typically involves either a shortened 1st metatarsal or an elongated 2nd metatarsal bone.

- The result shifts weight bearing to the 2nd metatarsal instead of along the 1st metatarsal.
- Results in pain throughout the foot during ambulation.

Morton's foot may result in **Morton's neuroma**.

- The problem is usually with the nerve between the 3rd and 4th metatarsal heads.
- Pain radiates to 3rd and 4th toes.
- A neuroma is an abnormal growth on a nerve.
- Tight-fitting shoes may be the cause. Going barefoot may help.
- This condition is best cared for by a physician.

Notes

Arch Problems

There are two groups of arch problems: pes planus and pes cavus.

- Pes planus related to pronation.

  - Excessive pronation can cause difficulties in the navicular bone and some of the joints around the ankle.
  - Arch taping has limited effectiveness.
  - Corrective arch orthoses may be beneficial.

- Pes cavas associated with plantar fasciitis and clawing of the toes.

  - Athlete may benefit from orthotic device.

Bunions

Bunions are uncommon in high school and college athletes.

- Can be inflamed bursae or bone or joint deformities.

- Can be caused by improperly fitting shoes.

- Chronic bunion should be evaluated by physician.

Blisters & Calluses

Blisters and calluses are very common formations, resulting from friction between layers of skin.

- When a blister forms, fluid collects between skin layers, occasionally the fluid will contain blood.

- If the blister is large, it should be drained and the area padded to prevent further friction.

- When draining a blister, it is best to leave top layer of skin in place.

- Use sterile instruments and wear latex gloves or some other barrier to avoid contact with athlete's body fluid.

Notes

Ronald P. Pfeiffer and Brent C. Mangus
Concepts of Athletic Training FOURTH EDITION

Blisters & Calluses (continued)

NSC First Aid Procedures

- Wash area with soap and warm water; sterilize area with rubbing alcohol.
- Use sterile needle to puncture the base of the blister and drain by applying light pressure. Process may need to be repeated during the first 24 hours.
- Do not remove the top of the blister.
- Apply antibiotic ointment to the top and cover with sterile dressing.
- Check daily for signs of infection (redness or pus).
- After 3-7 days, remove the top of blister and apply antibiotic ointment and sterile dressing.
- Watch for signs of infection. Pad area with gauze pads or moleskin.

Ronald P. Pfeiffer and Brent C. Mangus
Concepts of Athletic Training FOURTH EDITION

Toe Injuries

Common injuries are torn off nails or hematoma formation under the nail.

- Collection of blood under nail needs to be released.
- Use commercially available nail bore to drill small hole in nail to release blood.

Ingrown toenails may result from improperly fitting shoes.

- Soak affected toe in warm antibacterial solution.
- Elevate toenail by placing a small cotton roll under it and leave in place as nail grows.
- Have athlete obtain shoes that fit more comfortably.

Ronald P. Pfeiffer and Brent C. Mangus
Concepts of Athletic Training FOURTH EDITION

Basic Taping

1.
2.
3.

Notes

Ronald P. Pfeiffer and Brent C. Mangus
Concepts of Athletic Training FOURTH EDITION

Basic Taping (continued)

4.

5.

6.

Ronald P. Pfeiffer and Brent C. Mangus
Concepts of Athletic Training FOURTH EDITION

Basic Taping (continued)

7.

8.

9.

Ronald P. Pfeiffer and Brent C. Mangus
Concepts of Athletic Training FOURTH EDITION

Basic Taping (continued)

10.

11.

12.

Notes

_____
_____
_____
_____
_____
_____
_____
_____
_____
_____
_____

Ronald P. Pfeiffer and Brent C. Mangus

Concepts of Athletic Training FOURTH EDITION

Basic Taping (concluded)

13.

14.

15.

Chapter 17: Skin Conditions in Sports

Notes

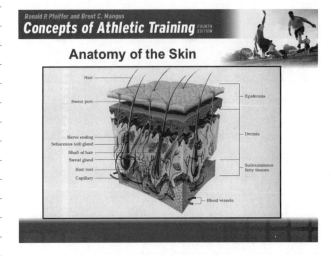

Anatomy of the Skin (continued)

The skin is largest organ of the body.

- Two major layers are the dermis and epidermis.
- Subcutaneous fat helps insulate the body from the environment.
- Skin thickness varies regionally; thickest skin is on the soles of the feet and palms of the hands.

Skin's functions include:

- Protection from environment.
- Maintenance of body's fluid balance.
- Protection against disease organisms. Temperature regulation.
- Housing for sensory nerves.
- Production of vitamin D.

Ronald P. Pfeiffer and Brent C. Mangus

Concepts of Athletic Training FOURTH EDITION

Anatomy of the Skin (continued)

Skin Damage

- External trauma resulting in wounds
- Exposure to UV light
- Temperature extremes -- hot or cold
- Pathogenic organisms -- bacteria, viruses, fungi
- Allergies

Ronald P. Pfeiffer and Brent C. Mangus

Concepts of Athletic Training FOURTH EDITION

Wounds

Wound Care

Primary goals of wound care are:
- Control bleeding.
- Prevent infection.

Primary concern when rendering first aid is avoidance of exposure to whole blood that may transmit HIV or HBV.

The majority of wounds in sports are abrasions, lacerations, and incisions.
- Turf burn is a form of abrasion associated with artificial grass surfaces.

Ronald P. Pfeiffer and Brent C. Mangus

Concepts of Athletic Training FOURTH EDITION

Wound Care (continued)

Treatment of wounds is a two-phase process.
- Initial first aid is **control bleeding**.
- Protect area with dressing.

Initial treatment follows NSC protocol.
- Take precautions against HIV and HBV.
  - Wear latex gloves and dispose of waste in storage container for biohazardous materials.
- Remove clothing and/or equipment around wound.

Ronald P. Pfeiffer and Brent C. Mangus
Concepts of Athletic Training FOURTH EDITION

Wound Treatment Protocol

- Apply direct pressure to control bleeding by applying some type of sterile dressing.
- If dressing becomes blood soaked, add more dressing on top. Do not remove blood-soaked dressings.
- If bleeding is severe and does not respond to direct pressure, use elevation in combination with direct pressure.

Ronald P. Pfeiffer and Brent C. Mangus
Concepts of Athletic Training FOURTH EDITION

Wound Treatment Protocol (continued)

- Increased hemorrhage control can be achieved by application of pressure bandage over either brachial or femoral arteries, depending on wound location.

  - Once pressure is applied to these points, it should not be removed until athlete is under physician's care.

  - Tourniquet should be applied only as a last resort.

- All materials used to treat the wound should be stored for later disposal in a properly identified **biohazardous** material container.

Ronald P. Pfeiffer and Brent C. Mangus
Concepts of Athletic Training FOURTH EDITION

Wound Care

At the time of initial injury, a decision must be made regarding continued participation.
- Consider health and safety of the athlete as well as risk to others.
- Once bleeding has stopped, apply commercially made dressing held in place by adhesive bandage.

Lacerations and incisions, particularly those to the scalp and face merit special attention because of potential cosmetic impact.

General rule: Any wound that is below dermal layer and more than 1 cm in length should be seen by a physician, especially if it is on the face.

Notes

_____

_____

_____

_____

_____

_____

_____

_____

_____

_____

_____

_____

_____

_____

_____

_____

_____

_____

_____

_____

_____

_____

_____

_____

_____

_____

_____

_____

_____

_____

_____

_____

_____

_____

_____

_____

_____

_____

_____

_____

Guidelines for Cleaning Wounds

- Personnel caring for wound should wear latex gloves.
- Wash wound with sterile gauze pad saturated with soap and water.
- A 3% solution of hydrogen peroxide may be used to clear away clotted blood.
- Flush with a lot of water and dry with sterile gauze.
- Clean around wound with isopropyl alcohol; do not apply the alcohol directly to the wound.

NSC Guidelines for Cleaning Wounds (continued)

- **DO NOT** apply Mercurochrome, Merthiolate, or iodine to wounds.
- Apply a sterile, dry dressing and hold in place with some type of clean bandage.
- Severe wounds should be treated for control of bleeding and referred immediately for medical evaluation.

HIV/HBV and the Athlete

HIV and **HBV** are bloodborne infections.
- Anyone who is sexually active is at risk.
- Athletes injecting steroids and sharing needles are also at risk.
- Any time a person infected with HIV sustains a bleeding wound, the possibility of transmission of exists.
- The prudent coach should follow basic preventive guidelines for HIV and HBV transmission, as outlined by OSHA (see **Time Out 17.1** on page 250).

Ronald P. Pfeiffer and Brent C. Mangus

Concepts of Athletic Training FOURTH EDITION

HIV/HBV and the Athlete (continued)

- Coaches are at risk because they are often exposed to bloody towels, water bottles, playing surfaces, and blood-soaked bandaging materials.
- Participants in wrestling, tackle football and boxing often sustain wounds.
    - Coaches and officials should take precautions and remove players from participation when excessive bleeding is evident.
- Education of athletes, coaches, and parents about HIV and HBV is essential.

Ronald P. Pfeiffer and Brent C. Mangus

Concepts of Athletic Training FOURTH EDITION

Other Skin Conditions

Ultraviolet Light-Related Skin Problems

- Outdoor sports played during summer often expose large areas of skin to harmful rays of the sun.
- Summer sportswear typically does NOT cover arms and legs.
    - In swimming and diving, major portions of skin are unprotected.
- Evidence indicates even a minor sunburn can be harmful.

Ronald P. Pfeiffer and Brent C. Mangus

Concepts of Athletic Training FOURTH EDITION

Ultraviolet Light-Related Skin Problems (continued)

- Although both UVA and UVB are harmful, UVB seems more related to the development of skin problems.

- Individuals with lighter skin, red hair, and freckles are at higher risk for skin damage.

- Exposure to sun at any time can result in sunburn, but most dangerous times are between 10:00 A.M. and 2:00 P.M.

Notes

_____
_____
_____
_____
_____
_____
_____
_____
_____
_____
_____
_____
_____
_____
_____
_____
_____
_____
_____
_____
_____
_____
_____
_____
_____
_____
_____
_____
_____
_____
_____
_____
_____
_____
_____
_____
_____
_____

Ronald P. Pfeiffer and Brent C. Mangus
Concepts of Athletic Training FOURTH EDITION

Ultraviolet Light-Related Skin Problems (continued)

Sunburn has two clinical phases.

- Immediate erythema phase involves reddening of the skin.
- Delayed erythema phase develops within a few hours of exposure, peaking at 24 hours.
- Most cases involve mild discomfort.
- Severe forms include blister formation, chills, and gastrointestinal distress.

Ronald P. Pfeiffer and Brent C. Mangus
Concepts of Athletic Training FOURTH EDITION

Ultraviolet Light-Related Skin Problems (continued)

Prevention and Care of Sunburn

- The primary concern is to protect exposed skin when outdoors.
- Apply commercially prepared sunscreen.
  - Emphasis on ears, nose, lips, back of the neck, forehead, forearms, and hands.
- Sunscreen products should have a sun protection factor (SPF) rating of at least 15.
- Sunblocks prevent light from reaching skin. They contain zinc oxide or titanium dioxide.

Ronald P. Pfeiffer and Brent C. Mangus
Concepts of Athletic Training FOURTH EDITION

Ultraviolet Light-Related Skin Problems (continued)

- Sunscreen products contain chemicals which absorb or reflect UVA or UVB.
  - These chemicals may include PABA, cinnamates, salicylates, and benzophenone-3.
- For best results, apply sunscreen in advance of exposure and reapply every 60 minutes.
- Treatment of sunburn is symptomatic; apply topical anesthetic as well as skin lotion to relieve burning and dryness.
  - In severe cases, medical referral is warranted.

Ronald P. Pfeiffer and Brent C. Mangus

Concepts of Athletic Training FOURTH EDITION

Skin Infections

- Various organisms cause skin infections, including fungi, bacteria, and viruses.
- May be symptoms of more serious infections or allergic conditions including Lyme disease, herpes, or contact dermatitis.

Tinea (ringworm) is a fungal infection that often affects the groin (tinea cruris), feet (tinea pedis), and scalp (tinea capitus).

- Signs and symptoms include small brownish-red elevated lesions that tend to be circular in shape.
- Itching and pain is associated with tinea pedis and tinea cruris.
- Tinea pedis often includes cracking between toes, oozing and crusting lesions, and scaly skin.

Ronald P. Pfeiffer and Brent C. Mangus

Concepts of Athletic Training FOURTH EDITION

Skin Infections (continued)

Tinea Treatment

- Keep the affected area clean and dry.
- Apply over-the-counter topical treatment.
- Apply a moisture-absorbing powder to the area.
- Wear clothing made of natural fibers such as cotton.

Tinea versicolor (TV) is a fungal infection that occurs most often during warm weather, and the infection typically involves teenagers and young adults.

- Signs and symptoms include circular lesions that appear lighter or darker than adjacent skin.

Ronald P. Pfeiffer and Brent C. Mangus

Concepts of Athletic Training FOURTH EDITION

Skin Infections (continued)

- TV lesions usually appear on upper trunk, neck, and abdomen.
- Treatment involves prescription drugs with weeks or months required for cure.

Bacterial Skin Infections

Bacterial infections are common in sports that involve close physical contact.

- Bacterial infections are collectively called pyoderma (pus producing-infections of the skin).
- *Staphylococcus aureus* and *Streptococcus* infections are common in sports with close physical contact.
- *Staphylococcus aureus* causes furuncles, carbuncles, and folliculitis.
- *Streptococcus* causes impetigo and cellulitis.

Notes

Ronald P. Pfeiffer and Brent C. Mangus
Concepts of Athletic Training *FOURTH EDITION*

Bacterial Skin Infections (continued)

The primary sign of all forms of pyoderma is a lesion that produces pus.

Any athlete with such lesions should be removed from participation and referred to a physician for medical evaluation.

Treatment is described in **Time Out 17.2** on page 253.

Ronald P. Pfeiffer and Brent C. Mangus
Concepts of Athletic Training *FOURTH EDITION*

Viral Skin Infections

Common viral infections among athletes are plantar warts and herpes gladiatorum.

- **Warts** are common among the general public. Warts are caused by human papillomavirus (HPV)
  - Majority of plantar warts are caused by HPV-1 and HPV-4.
  - Infection is contagious.
  - The sign is an abnormal buildup of epidermis around the region of infection.

Ronald P. Pfeiffer and Brent C. Mangus
Concepts of Athletic Training *FOURTH EDITION*

Viral Skin Infections (continued)

- Plantar warts are named for their location; they occur on the bottom of the foot.
- Treatment includes direct application of chemicals as well as removal by surgery.

Notes

_____

_____

_____

_____

_____

_____

_____

_____

_____

_____

_____

_____

_____

_____

_____

_____

_____

_____

_____

_____

_____

_____

_____

_____

_____

_____

_____

_____

_____

_____

_____

Concepts of Athletic Training — FOURTH EDITION
Ronald P. Pfeiffer and Brent C. Mangus

Viral Skin Infections (continued)

Herpes Gladiatorum

- **Herpes gladiatorum** is caused by HSV-1.
- Lesions are associated with physical trauma, sunburn, emotional disturbances, fatigue, or infection.
- Virus may remain dormant for months or years.
- Signs and systems include:
  - Development of a blister-like lesion.
  - Open draining lesions that may persist, then become crusted and begin to heal.
  - General fatigue, body aches, and inflammation of lymph glands.

Concepts of Athletic Training — FOURTH EDITION
Ronald P. Pfeiffer and Brent C. Mangus

Viral Skin Infections (continued)

- Herpes infections **MUST** be controlled by removal from participation until lesions are healed.

- Prescription drugs may be helpful.

- For other precautions regarding HSV-1, see **Time Out 17.3** on page 255.

Concepts of Athletic Training — FOURTH EDITION
Ronald P. Pfeiffer and Brent C. Mangus

Allergic Reactions

Allergies:

- Can result from exposure to a wide variety of chemical agents.
- Can be skin reactions that result from contact with chemicals.

  - "Contact dermatitis" can result from contact with plants, particularly poison ivy, sumac, and poison oak.

Notes

_____

_____

_____

_____

_____

_____

_____

_____

_____

_____

_____

_____

_____

_____

_____

_____

_____

_____

_____

_____

_____

_____

_____

_____

_____

_____

_____

_____

_____

_____

_____

_____

_____

_____

_____

_____

_____

_____

_____

_____

Ronald P. Pfeiffer and Brent C. Mangus

Concepts of Athletic Training FOURTH EDITION

Allergic Reactions (continued)

Contact with poison ivy, poison oak, and poison sumac result in allergic reactions in 90% of adults.

- Offending chemicals are in the sap.
- Average time from exposure to reaction is 24 to 48 hours.
- Early signs and symptoms include itching and redness of affected skin.
- Later blisters develop.
- Healing requires 1 to 2 weeks.

Ronald P. Pfeiffer and Brent C. Mangus

Concepts of Athletic Training FOURTH EDITION

Allergic Reactions (continued)

- Susceptible athletes should learn to recognize poison ivy, poison oak, and poison sumac.
- Avoid areas where these plants grow.
- Outdoor events, such as cross-country running, should be staged away from high risk areas.
- **Time Out 17.4** on page 255 lists ways to prevent plant-related allergies.

Ronald P. Pfeiffer and Brent C. Mangus

Concepts of Athletic Training FOURTH EDITION

Allergic Reactions (continued)

Allergies related to chemicals in clothing and sports equipment have recently received attention.

- Allergies to rubber, latex, topical analgesics, resins, and epoxy are common.
- Some people are allergic to synthetic rubber that is in sports shoes, swim caps, goggles, and earplugs.

An athlete suspected of having an allergic dermatitis should be referred to a dermatologist.

Chapter 18: Thermal Injuries

Notes

Concepts of Athletic Training FOURTH EDITION
Ronald P. Pfeiffer
Brent C. Mangus

Chapter 18

Thermal Injuries

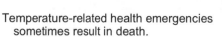

Ronald P. Pfeiffer and Brent C. Mangus
Concepts of Athletic Training FOURTH EDITION

Thermal Injuries

Temperature-related health emergencies sometimes result in death.

– The majority, if not all, of these deaths could be prevented if the environment is taken into consideration before allowing an event to begin.

– Normal core body temperature ranges from between 98.0°F to 98.6°F (oral).

– Heat is a byproduct of metabolism.

Ronald P. Pfeiffer and Brent C. Mangus
Concepts of Athletic Training FOURTH EDITION

Thermal Injuries (continued)

– Exercise increases metabolic rate and can elevate body temperature to 104°F.

– Excess heat **MUST** be eliminated.

– Thermoregulation is controlled primarily by the hypothalamus in the brain.

Notes

_____

_____

_____

_____

_____

_____

_____

_____

_____

_____

_____

_____

physiological changes _p. 260_

_____

- core temp ↓   paper

- skin temp ↓   paper

- sweat ↑

_____ Con. Acclimatization

_____

_____

_____

_____

_____

_____

_____

_____

_____

_____

_____

_____

_____

_____

Concepts of Athletic Training — Fourth Edition
Ronald P. Pfeiffer and Brent C. Mangus

Thermoregulation

Excess body heat is lost through:

- Radiation.
- Conduction.
- Convection.
- **Evaporation**.
  - Evaporation is most efficient during exercise on dry land.
  - Evaporation can be reduced when humidity is high.
  - Coaches should **reduce** exercise demands during periods of high humidity and temperature.

Concepts of Athletic Training — Fourth Edition
Ronald P. Pfeiffer and Brent C. Mangus

Thermoregulation (continued)

Acclimatization is a process in which the body adjusts to continuous and significant climate change.

- The process can take 1 to 6 weeks.

In hot conditions, athletes need **4** to **10 L** of fluids daily to avoid dehydration.

- Athletes can lose 2% to 6% of their body weight during exercise.
- Fluid needs increase as the rate of sweating increases.

Concepts of Athletic Training — Fourth Edition
Ronald P. Pfeiffer and Brent C. Mangus

Dehydration

Minimal dehydration (less than 2% body weight loss) generally does not affect health or performance.

Signs and symptoms include:
- Dry mouth.
- Thirst.
- Irritability or crankiness.
- Headache.
- Dizziness.
- Excessive fatigue.
- Reduced physical performance.

Notes

Ronald P. Pfeiffer and Brent C. Mangus
Concepts of Athletic Training FOURTH EDITION

Dehydration (continued)

Management

- Remove athlete from participation and move him or her to cool location.

- Rehydrate with water or sports drink, preferably that is 50°F to 59°F.

- If dehydration is minor (less than 2% body weight lost) and symptoms are relieved, athlete can return to participation.

- If symptoms persist, seek medical attention.

Ronald P. Pfeiffer and Brent C. Mangus
Concepts of Athletic Training FOURTH EDITION

Heat Cramps

Heat cramps generally develop in the muscles being exercised.

- The physiology of heat cramps is unclear, but it is probably related to water and mineral loss that result from sweating.

Signs and symptoms include:

- Severe muscle cramps in arms or legs.
- Muscle cramps in the abdominal muscles.
- Profuse sweating.

Ronald P. Pfeiffer and Brent C. Mangus
Concepts of Athletic Training FOURTH EDITION

Heat Cramps (continued)

Management

- Athlete should immediately cease exercising.
- Give athlete fluids to consume, either water or commercially prepared sports drinks.
- Have athlete perform static stretching of involved muscles.

Notes

_____

_____

_____

_____

_____

_____

_____

_____

_____

_____

_____

_____

_____

_____

_____

_____

_____

_____

_____

_____

_____

_____

_____

_____

_____

_____

_____

_____

_____

_____

_____

_____

_____

_____

_____

_____

_____

_____

_____

_____

Ronald P. Pfeiffer and Brent C. Mangus
Concepts of Athletic Training (FOURTH EDITION)

Heat Exhaustion

Although heat exhaustion is not a life-threatening condition, it can be a precursor to heatstroke, a true medical emergency.

- Heat exhaustion causes generalized fatigue during exercise when excessive body fluid losses occur.
- Coach should constantly monitor athletes for signs and symptoms of heat exhaustion when they must practice in extreme heat and humidity.

Ronald P. Pfeiffer and Brent C. Mangus
Concepts of Athletic Training (FOURTH EDITION)

Heat Exhaustion (continued)

The signs and symptoms of heat exhaustion include:

- Moist, clammy skin.
- Profuse sweating.
- General muscle fatigue and/or cramps.
- Nausea or related GI distress.
- Dizziness, and occasionally, loss of consciousness.
- Severe thirst.
- Headache.
- Increased respiratory rate and rapid pulse.
- Body temperature that ranges from 97°F to 104°F.

Ronald P. Pfeiffer and Brent C. Mangus
Concepts of Athletic Training (FOURTH EDITION)

Heat Exhaustion (continued)

Management

- Athlete should immediately cease exercising.
- If athlete is not nauseous, give fluids immediately, preferably cool water or sports drink.
- Move athlete to cool location and place into a supine position with legs elevated 8 to 12 inches.
- Loosen athlete's clothing and cool with wet towels or ice packs.
- If athlete is not fully recovered within 30 minutes, seek medical attention.
- Do **NOT** allow athlete to return to participation for the remainder of the day.

Ronald P. Pfeiffer and Brent C. Mangus

Concepts of Athletic Training FOURTH EDITION

Heat Stroke

Heat stroke occurs when the body is unable to cool itself and a radical elevation of body temperature occurs, sometimes exceeding 106°F.

Classic heatstroke occurs in obese, the chronically ill or elderly, or diabetics.

Exertional heatstroke occurs in athletes exercising in warm, humid conditions.

- This condition is usually related to excess body fluid losses combined with inadequate evaporative cooling.

Ronald P. Pfeiffer and Brent C. Mangus

Concepts of Athletic Training FOURTH EDITION

Heat Stroke (continued)

Signs and symptoms include:

- Sweating may or may not be present.
- Hot, dry skin or clammy skin.
- Mental confusion and possible loss of consciousness.
- GI distress, including nausea and vomiting.
- Severe motor disturbances and loss of coordination.
- Rapid and strong pulse.
- Rectal temperature higher than 104°F.

Ronald P. Pfeiffer and Brent C. Mangus

Concepts of Athletic Training FOURTH EDITION

Heat Stroke (continued)

Management

- Heat stroke is a true medical emergency. Death can result if not treated correctly and promptly.
- If EMS personnel, athletic trainer, or physician is present, cool the athlete using cold-water immersion.
- If the above personnel are not on site, summon EMS.
- If cold-water immersion is not possible, move athlete to a cool, humidity-controlled location.

Ronald P. Pfeiffer and Brent C. Mangus
Concepts of Athletic Training FOURTH EDITION

Heat Stroke (continued)

- Wrap athlete in wet towels or sheets, and place cold packs on neck, head, groin, or under armpits.
- Treat for shock and monitor body temperature. Do not allow temperature to drop below 102°F.
- Keep athlete in semi-seated position.

Ronald P. Pfeiffer and Brent C. Mangus
Concepts of Athletic Training FOURTH EDITION

Prevention of Exertional Heat Illnesses

Heat-related illness causing death is totally preventable.

- Utilize a weight chart to determine if an athlete is consuming enough fluids.
  - For every pound of weight lost, the athlete should consume 24 oz. of fluid.
- The athlete should consume 17 to 20 oz. of fluids 2 to 3 hours before activity and an additional 7 to 10 oz. 10 to 20 minutes before the activity.

Heat Index Chart   p 262

Ronald P. Pfeiffer and Brent C. Mangus
Concepts of Athletic Training FOURTH EDITION

Prevention of Exertional Heat Illnesses (continued)

- The athlete should consume 7 to 10 oz. of fluids every 10 to 20 min. during the activity.
- Avoid heavy exertion during times of extreme heat (above 95°F) and humidity.
- Athlete should avoid wearing restrictive clothing.
  - Dark colors may facilitate heat buildup.
- Improved fitness levels have a position effect on the athlete's ability to function in extreme conditions. Developing tolerance (acclimatization) requires 1 to 6 weeks.

Notes

_____

_____

_____

_____

_____

_____

_____

_____

_____

_____

_____

_____

_____

_____

_____

_____

_____

_____

_____

_____

_____

_____

_____

_____

_____

_____

_____

_____

_____

_____

_____

_____

_____

Ronald P. Pfeiffer and Brent C. Mangus

Concepts of Athletic Training FOURTH EDITION

Cold-Related Health Problems

Hypothermia involves the rapid loss of body heat, resulting in total body cooling.

- Mild hypothermia begins when the core body temperature drops to 95°F.
- Extremely lean athletes are at risk because they have little insulating body fat.
- A combination of wind and moisture facilitates hypothermia, even if temperature is well above freezing.

Ronald P. Pfeiffer and Brent C. Mangus

Concepts of Athletic Training FOURTH EDITION

Cold-Related Health Problems (continued)

Signs and symptoms include:

- In **mild** cases, shivering, loss of motor function, speech slurring, confusion, and memory loss.

- In **severe** cases, lack of shivering, stiff muscles, blue skin, and decreased respiration and pulse.

  • Athlete will be semiconscious or unconscious.

Ronald P. Pfeiffer and Brent C. Mangus

Concepts of Athletic Training FOURTH EDITION

Cold-Related Health Problems (continued)

Management of Mild Hypothermia

- Move athlete to a source of heat and out of the cold.
- Remove any wet clothing.
- Wrap in warm, dry clothing or blankets.
- Warm athlete with an electric blanket or hot packs placed around head and neck, armpits, groin, and chest.

Notes

Cold-Related Health Problems (continued)

Management of Severe Hypothermia (body temperature is below 90°F)

- Transport athlete immediately to a health care facility.
- **DO NOT** attempt to re-warm.
- Prevent further heat loss by moving athlete to a warm place and by gently removing cold wet clothing.
- Monitor vital signs.

Cold-Related Health Problems (continued)

Prevention of Hypothermia

- Assess risk by learning to use a wind-chill chart. (See **Table 18.3** on page 267.)
- Don't take long outdoor trips alone. Tell someone where you are going and when you expect to reach your destination.
- Learn to recognize early warning signs of hypothermia.

p. 265

Drugs + Alcohol etc...
Heatstroke

Cold-Related Health Problems (continued)

Prevention of Hypothermia (continued)

- Dress appropriately for cold weather.
  - New synthetic materials wick body moisture away from the skin while retaining body heat.
- Make sure to remain hydrated and consume adequate calories to generate body heat.
  - Avoid using drugs such as alcohol.

Notes

_____
_____
_____
_____
_____
_____
_____
_____
_____
_____
_____
_____
_____
_____
_____
_____
_____
_____
_____
_____
_____
_____
_____
_____
_____
_____
_____
_____
_____
_____
_____
_____
_____
_____
_____
_____
_____
_____

Ronald P. Pfeiffer and Brent C. Mangus
Concepts of Athletic Training FOURTH EDITION

Frostbite and Frostnip

Frostbite occurs when tissues freeze after excessive exposure to cold.

- Symptoms include feeling of burning and pain, followed by progressive loss of sensation.

Frostnip is less severe and involves only outer skin layers.

These conditions usually involve the nose, ears, fingers, and feet.

Ronald P. Pfeiffer and Brent C. Mangus
Concepts of Athletic Training FOURTH EDITION

Frostbite and Frostnip (continued)

- Severe damage occurs when frostbitten tissue is thawed and refrozen.

- During outdoor activities in freezing temperatures, athletes need to be vigilant for early warning signs.

Ronald P. Pfeiffer and Brent C. Mangus
Concepts of Athletic Training FOURTH EDITION

Frostbite and Frostnip (continued)

Signs and symptoms of superficial freezing include:
- White or grayish-yellow skin color.
- Pain may occur initially and later subside.
- Affected part feels very cold and numb.
- Tingling, stinging, or aching sensation.
- Skin surface feels hard and crusty.
- Underlying tissue feels soft when depressed gently and firmly.

Notes

Frostbite and Frostnip
(continued)

Signs and symptoms of deep freezing include:

Affected body part feels hard, solid, and cannot be depressed.

- Blisters appear in 12 to 36 hours.
- Affected body part is cold with pale, waxy skin.
- The painfully cold body part suddenly stops hurting.
- **First Aid**
  - See **Time Out 18.2** on page 268.

Frostbite and Frostnip
(continued)

First Aid

- Get medical attention immediately.
- Do NOT attempt re-warming.
- If medical help is delayed, slow re-warming is necessary.
- Remove clothing/restricting items such as rings.
- Place in warm water (102-106 deg. F).

Cold Urticaria

- Cold urticaria is a localized skin reaction to cold that involves edema and severe itching.
- Involves areas of skin exposed to cold.
- Mechanism is unknown; it may be an allergic reaction.
- Athletes with mononucleosis, chickenpox, or hepatitis are more susceptible.
- Athletes taking penicillin or oral contraceptives also have a higher incidence.

Concepts of Athletic Training FOURTH EDITION
Ronald P. Pfeiffer and Brent C. Mangus

Cold Urticaria (continued)

- Symptoms are self-limiting and resolve within a few hours after re-warming.
- Medical referral may be warranted if symptoms recur.
- Antihistamines can control edema and itching.
- Certain types of outdoor clothing may protect the skin better than other types.

what is going on?

what's up?

Notes

**Concepts of
Athletic Training** FOURTH EDITION
Ronald P. Pfeiffer
Brent C. Mangus

Chapter 19

Other Medical Concerns

Ronald P. Pfeiffer and Brent C. Mangus
Concepts of Athletic Training FOURTH EDITION

Exercise and Infectious Disease

Infectious diseases are caused by some type of microorganism: viruses, bacteria, fungi, or protozoa.

- Although exercise improves resistance to infection, athletes are vulnerable to the same infections that affect the general population.
- The majority of conditions affecting athletes involve either the respiratory or gastrointestinal systems.

Ronald P. Pfeiffer and Brent C. Mangus
Concepts of Athletic Training FOURTH EDITION

Respiratory Infections

Respiratory infections can be categorized as either URI or LRI.

- URI involves nose, throat, ears, sinuses, tonsils, and associated lymph glands.
- LRI involves lungs, bronchi, and larynx.
- Majority of both types of infections are caused by viruses.

Notes

Upper Respiratory Infections

- URI produces symptoms known as the common cold or rhinitis.
- Signs and symptoms include sore throat, stuffy nose, mild cough, mild fatigue, and fever.
  - URIs are generally self-limiting.
  - Antibiotic therapy is ineffective against viral infections.
- Athletes should be instructed **NOT** to borrow drugs from another person as allergic or toxic reactions may result.
  - Athletes with URI can normally continue to participate unless symptoms place them at obvious risk.

Upper Respiratory Infections (continued)

URIs that persist for more than a few days may involve bacterial infections, such as streptococci.

- Symptoms of bacterial infections are more severe with visible lesions in the back of the throat, severe sore throat, swollen lymph glands in neck or throat, fever and chills.

- Athletes with signs and symptoms of bacterial infection should be removed from participation and referred to a physician.

Lower Respiratory Infections

LRIs can impair athletic performance for several weeks.

- Normally LRIs involve viral infections of the bronchi.
- Signs and symptoms include cough, fever, and malaise.
- Athletes in aerobic sports will be negatively affected.

An athlete with a LRI should be isolated from other athletes and referred to physician.

- **Bronchitis** and **pneumonia** are serious LRIs.
  - Diagnosis of either must be made by a physician.

Notes

Ronald P. Pfeiffer and Brent C. Mangus
Concepts of Athletic Training FOURTH EDITION

Gastrointestinal Infections

GI illnesses may be viral, bacterial, or protozoan infections.

- This group of illnesses is known as **gastroenteritis** (inflammation of the stomach and intestines).
- Symptoms include abdominal cramping, nausea (often with vomiting), fever, chills, and diarrhea.

Ronald P. Pfeiffer and Brent C. Mangus
Concepts of Athletic Training FOURTH EDITION

Gastrointestinal Infections (continued)

- An athlete with symptoms of gastroenteritis should NOT be allowed to participate.
- Monitor symptoms for 24 hours.
- If symptoms persist or get worse, refer to a physician.
- Any athlete complaining of severe diarrhea or bloody stools should be referred to a physician.

Ronald P. Pfeiffer and Brent C. Mangus
Concepts of Athletic Training FOURTH EDITION

Lyme Disease

Lyme disease is a bacterial infection transmitted by the common deer tick (sometimes called bear tick in western United States).

- Lyme disease has surpassed Rocky Mountain spotted fever as the most prevalent tick-borne infectious disease in the country.
- Disease is transmitted by a tick bite.
- Incubation period ranges from three days to one month.
- The early symptom is a circular area of reddened skin at the site of the bite.

Lyme Disease (continued)

- Other symptoms include fever, chills, general aches and pains, and general fatigue.
- If untreated, the disease can become systemic and affect the heart and CNS.
  - Majority of untreated cases develop arthritis, particularly affected the knee.
    - If untreated, the disease can persist for years.

Lyme Disease (continued)

- Athletes in high risk areas should check themselves for ticks.
  - Athlete may require assistance in hard-to-see areas such as back, back of neck and behind the ears.
- The deer tick is very small; if found on the body, remove immediately.
- **Time Out 19.2** on page 275 provides instructions for removing feeding ticks from skin safely.
- Treatment for Lyme disease involves antibiotics.

Infectious Mononucleosis

Infectious mononucleosis is an extremely common viral infection among young people in the United States.

- Initial symptoms include sore throat, fever, chills, enlarged lymph glands in the neck and jaw region, and extreme fatigue.
- As disease progresses, it can involve the liver and spleen.
- Transmission is typically by direct contact with discharge from an infected person's mouth.

Ronald P. Pfeiffer and Brent C. Mangus
Concepts of Athletic Training FOURTH EDITION

Infectious Mononucleosis (continued)

- Incubation is variable, usually 2 to 6 weeks.
- Treatment is symptomatic.
- In 40% to 60% of cases, splenomegaly occurs.
- Athletes with enlarged spleen and involved in combative sports are at risk for spleen rupture.

Ronald P. Pfeiffer and Brent C. Mangus
Concepts of Athletic Training FOURTH EDITION

Infectious Mononucleosis (continued)

- Spleen ruptures are most likely to occur between 4th and 21st day of illness.
  - Athletes with "mono" should never be allowed to participate during this period.
- Preventing the infection is difficult.
  - Athletes should know that kissing transmits the virus that causes the infection.
  - As a general precaution, athletes should not share towels, water bottles or other beverage containers, clothing, and any other objects that could be contaminated with the virus.

Ronald P. Pfeiffer and Brent C. Mangus
Concepts of Athletic Training FOURTH EDITION

Hepatitis Infection

- **HAV** or **HBV** are both serious. HBV considered potentially life threatening.
  - HAV is transmitted via feces, which is a problem for food handlers.
  - HBV transmitted through blood and sexual fluids.
    - IV drug users can become infected through contaminated needles.
  - Incubation for HAV is 15 to 50 days; HBV is 45 to 160 days.

Notes

_____

_____

_____

_____

_____

_____

_____

_____

_____

_____

_____

_____

_____

_____

_____

_____

_____

_____

_____

_____

_____

_____

_____

_____

_____

_____

_____

_____

_____

_____

_____

_____

_____

_____

_____

Ronald P. Pfeiffer and Brent C. Mangus
Concepts of Athletic Training FOURTH EDITION

Hepatitis Infection (continued)

Signs and symptoms for both types of infection include:

- Nausea, abdominal pain, vomiting, fever, and malaise.

If untreated, both types will involve the liver and result in jaundice.

- Liver damage is possible.

Treatment is limited.
- HAV can be treated with immediate inoculation with ISG to provide passive immunity.
  - ISG may be effective against HBV.

Athletes with HAV or HBV should be removed from participation.

Ronald P. Pfeiffer and Brent C. Mangus
Concepts of Athletic Training FOURTH EDITION

Exercise-Induced Asthma

Exercise-induced asthma (EIA) is a temporary increase in airway resistance that occurs after strenuous exercise.

- Highest incidence (80%) is found among chronic asthmatics.
  - EIA affects 12% - 15% of the general population.
- Airway restriction or bronchospasm occurs within minutes of on cessation of exercise.
- Exact cause is unknown. Major theories include:
  - Rapid respiration may cause drying of mucus, resulting in bronchoconstriction.
  - Dilation of bronchial vessels causes narrowing of airways.

Ronald P. Pfeiffer and Brent C. Mangus
Concepts of Athletic Training FOURTH EDITION

Exercise-Induced Asthma (continued)

- EIA is common among susceptible runners and less common among cyclists or walkers.
- Indoor swimming less likely to stimulate an attack.
- Signs and symptoms include:
  - Coughing and chest tightness.
  - Shortness of breath.
  - Fatigue and stomachache (in children).
  - Some athletes become alarmed.

_____

p 273

drugs banned

Ronald P. Pfeiffer and Brent C. Mangus
Concepts of Athletic Training FOURTH EDITION

Exercise-Induced Asthma
(continued)

Management

- Administration of drugs that prevent airway restriction or bronchospasm.
  - Normally given with an inhaler.
- Coaches should be aware of athletes on roster who have asthma.
  - Athletes should avoid drugs that are banned.
- Highly susceptible athletes should avoid high-risk activities.
- Sports that involve short bursts of activity followed with rest periods are excellent alternatives.

Ronald P. Pfeiffer and Brent C. Mangus
Concepts of Athletic Training FOURTH EDITION

The Athlete with Diabetes

Diabetes is characterized by the inability to appropriately metabolize CHO.

- Blood glucose levels in the diabetic person may fluctuate widely from hyper- to hypoglycemia.
- Ability to manufacture or utilize insulin NOT possible for the athlete with type 1 diabetes.
- Exercise is considered beneficial for children with insulin-dependent diabetes.
  - Problems can arise if exercise intensity, diet, and insulin dosage are not carefully monitored.

Ronald P. Pfeiffer and Brent C. Mangus
Concepts of Athletic Training FOURTH EDITION

The Athlete with Diabetes
(continued)

- The diabetic athlete needs to anticipate insulin requirement to maintain blood glucose levels between 100 to 200 mg/dL.

- If athlete does NOT correct insulin level for exercise and there is too little insulin for the amount of blood glucose, **hyperglycemia** results.

  - In some cases, however, this athlete may have the opposite reaction. Liver glucose production decreases while muscle demand increases, leading to **hypoglycemia**.

Notes

The Athlete with Diabetes (continued)

- Research indicates that exercise type may determine the type of insulin response.
  - Sustained, moderate-intensity exercise can help maintain or decrease blood glucose level.
    - Diabetics involved in triathlons or marathons may need to decrease their insulin levels and increase caloric intake before race or training session.
  - Brief bouts of high-intensity exercise can increase blood glucose levels.
    - Diabetics in sports such as tackle football, soccer, and basketball need to be monitored to avoid hyperglycemia.

The Athlete with Diabetes (continued)

- Athletes with diabetes must learn to monitor their blood glucose.
- These athletes must be able to estimate their caloric requirements and adjust their insulin and diets accordingly.
- Coaches and parents need to be able to recognize early signs and symptoms of both hypoglycemia and hyperglycemia.

The Athlete with Diabetes (continued)

The signs and symptoms of **hyperglycemia** develop slowly and include:

- Fruity breath odor.
- Extreme thirst and need to urinate.
- Nausea and/or vomiting.
- Loss of consciousness.

Management

- Summon EMS.
- Treat for shock and monitor vital signs.

Notes

_____

_____

_____

_____

_____

_____

_____

_____

_____

_____

_____

_____

_____

_____

_____

_____

_____

_____

_____

_____

_____

_____

_____

_____

_____

_____

_____

_____

_____

_____

_____

_____

_____

_____

_____

_____

_____

Ronald P. Pfeiffer and Brent C. Mangus

Concepts of Athletic Training FOURTH EDITION

The Athlete with Diabetes (continued)

The signs and symptoms of **hypoglycemia** develop quickly and include:

- Unusual behavior.
- Profuse perspiration.
- Loss of motor coordination.
- Extreme hunger.

Management

- If athlete is conscious, immediately give food or beverage that contains sugar.
- If no improvement within minutes, summon EMS.
- Treat for shock and monitor vital signs.

Ronald P. Pfeiffer and Brent C. Mangus

Concepts of Athletic Training FOURTH EDITION

Epilepsy and Sports Participation

Epilepsy is a brain disorder characterized by seizures that take many forms and may involve motor systems, perceptions, even moods of the athlete.

- Three forms of seizures are common.
  - Generalize tonic-clonic ("grand-mal" form) is characterized by generalized convulsions.
  - Absence attack (formerly "petit-mal") is characterized by a sudden loss of awareness combined with blank stare lasting only a few seconds.

Ronald P. Pfeiffer and Brent C. Mangus

Concepts of Athletic Training FOURTH EDITION

Epilepsy and Sports Participation (continued)

- Complex partial seizure is characterized by a sudden loss of contact with surroundings and unusual behavior that lasts up to 5 minutes.
- Coaches must address two major concerns:
  - The athlete's safety in their chosen sport(s).
  - First aid care in case of a seizure.
- Over half of epileptics on medication remain free from seizures and 30% have infrequent attacks.

Notes

_____

Ronald P. Pfeiffer and Brent C. Mangus
Concepts of Athletic Training _FOURTH EDITION_

Epilepsy and Sports Participation (continued)

- High risk activities include aquatic sports, sports in which falling is possible, and contact and collision sports.
- Participants in water sports should swim with a "buddy" and alert pool personnel of their condition.
- People with epilepsy should be discouraged from sports such as cycling, ice-skating or speed skating, skydiving, and horseback riding.

Ronald P. Pfeiffer and Brent C. Mangus
Concepts of Athletic Training _FOURTH EDITION_

Epilepsy and Sports Participation (continued)

- Athletes with epilepsy have no greater risk of injury while participating in contact/collision sports than other athletes.
  - There is no reason to exclude children with epilepsy from most school or community sports programs.
    - Participation can improve the self-esteem.
  - Coaching personnel need to educate all participants about epilepsy.

Ronald P. Pfeiffer and Brent C. Mangus
Concepts of Athletic Training _FOURTH EDITION_

Epilepsy and Sports Participation (continued)

First Aid

- In general, first aid involves protection from self-injury followed by psychological support after the seizure.
- See **Time Out 19.4** on page 282 for treatment protocols.

Notes

Concepts of Athletic Training FOURTH EDITION
Ronald P. Pfeiffer
Brent C. Mangus

Chapter 20

The Adolescent Athlete:
Special Medical Concerns

Ronald P. Pfeiffer and Brent C. Mangus
Concepts of Athletic Training FOURTH EDITION

Youth Sports in America

Physical educators and other teachers now play a diminishing role in coaching school-sponsored sports. The parents and volunteers that took on these activities often have no formal training.

- Children play organized sports most often to have fun, make friends, develop skills, improve physical fitness, and gain role models.
- Withdrawal from high school sports is often due to lack of playing time, dislike of the coach, and overemphasis on competition.
- Attrition among elementary school participants results from lack of success and playing time, and the "absence of fun."

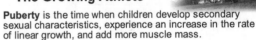

Ronald P. Pfeiffer and Brent C. Mangus
Concepts of Athletic Training FOURTH EDITION

The Growing Athlete

- **Puberty** is the time when children develop secondary sexual characteristics, experience an increase in the rate of linear growth, and add more muscle mass.
  - The average age that puberty begins is 10 years for girls and 12 years for boys.
    - In girls, the onset of breast development signals puberty.
    - In boys, increased testicular volume is the first sign of puberty.
  - The average boy experiences a doubling of his muscle mass between the ages of 10 and 17 years.
  - Longitudinal growth accelerates during puberty with peak height velocity attained at the average age of 12 years in girls and 14 years in boys.

Notes

Ronald P. Pfeiffer and Brent C. Mangus
Concepts of Athletic Training FOURTH EDITION

Growth

- Longitudinal bone growth arises from the physis (growth plate) located near the ends of long bones.
  - Bone growth ends once the physis closes. Average age of full skeletal development is approximately 14 years for girls and 16 years for boys.
- The physes, apophyses, and articular surfaces of long bones are key structures susceptible to injury in the adolescent.
- Skeletal muscles grow in size by responding to increasing forces. As bones progressively lengthen, the muscle become correspondingly longer.

Ronald P. Pfeiffer and Brent C. Mangus
Concepts of Athletic Training FOURTH EDITION

Injury Mechanisms

Two basic injury categories: **macrotrauma** and **microtrauma**.

- Macrotrauma results from a single, high-force traumatic event. Young athletes are more likely to suffer trauma to the growth plate.

- Microtrauma results from chronic, repetitive stress to local tissues. This type of injury is common in children and adolescents, representing the majority of injuries in young athletes.

Ronald P. Pfeiffer and Brent C. Mangus
Concepts of Athletic Training FOURTH EDITION

Ligament Injuries

- Severe ligamentous injuries are less common in adolescent athletes, occurring primarily due to laxity of the ligaments or plasticity of long bones.
- Tendon injuries are chronic, microtraumatic injuries to the immature apophysis, calcaneus, and medial humerus.
- Apophyseal injuries are often the result of multiple factors.

Notes

Concepts of Athletic Training FOURTH EDITION
Ronald P. Pfeiffer and Brent C. Mangus

Growth Plate Injuries

- Growth plate injuries have five injury patterns, the Salter-Harris type I fracture is the most common physis injury.
  - Injuries to the distal fibula and distal radius are the most common.
- Chronic, repetitive axial loading of a physis may lead to microvascular injury and resultant growth arrest.
  - This injury is commonly seen in gymnasts.

Concepts of Athletic Training FOURTH EDITION
Ronald P. Pfeiffer and Brent C. Mangus

Contributors to Injury

Intrinsic factors that contribute to injury include:

- The growing body's susceptibility to growth cartilage injuries.
- The decreased flexibility of the muscle-tendon unit.

Extrinsic factors that contribute to injury include:

- Cultural deconditioning that results in youth obesity.
- Training errors by coaches who do not have the requisite knowledge for instructing young athletes.
  - Many young athletes have a tendency toward overtraining.

Concepts of Athletic Training FOURTH EDITION
Ronald P. Pfeiffer and Brent C. Mangus

Contributors to Injuries (continued)

- Equipment should always be up-to-date and appropriate.
- Poor playing surfaces can put athletes at risk for injury.

Concepts of Athletic Training *FOURTH EDITION*
Ronald P. Pfeiffer and Brent C. Mangus

Injury Imitators

There are three principles when evaluating an injured adolescent for serious medical conditions that may be confused with musculoskeletal trauma. These include:

- Physical findings that are inconsistent with injury history.
- Unusual local symptoms.
- Systemic symptoms.

Concepts of Athletic Training *FOURTH EDITION*
Ronald P. Pfeiffer and Brent C. Mangus

Injury Imitators: Oncologic

- Adolescence is the peak age for occurrence of long bone tumors.
  - Symptoms may be mistaken for a traumatic etiology early in the course of illness. **Osteosarcomas** commonly arise in the metaphyses of the femur, tibia, and humerus.
- Ewing's sarcoma is typically found in the mid-shaft of long bones, but may arise in pelvis.
- Diagnosis is made by plain radiographs and biopsy.
- Treatment involves tumor excision and intensive chemotherapy.

Concepts of Athletic Training *FOURTH EDITION*
Ronald P. Pfeiffer and Brent C. Mangus

Injury Imitators: Rheumatologic

- Athlete complains of pain or swelling in more than one joint in the absence of a trauma.
- **Juvenile rheumatoid arthritis** must be considered.
- May result in severe low back and lower extremity pain as well as systemic symptoms (fever and rash).

Ronald P. Pfeiffer and Brent C. Mangus
Concepts of Athletic Training FOURTH EDITION

Injury Imitators: Infectious

Osteomyelitis may present similarly to bone tumors, with fever more common in the infection.

- The diagnosis is made by bone scan or MRI.
- Treatment involves 4 to 6 weeks of intravenous antibiotics.

Ronald P. Pfeiffer and Brent C. Mangus
Concepts of Athletic Training FOURTH EDITION

Injury Imitators: Neurovascular

Reflex neuropathic dystrophy (RND) is preceded by minor injury but involves severe pain and dysfunction, marked tenderness, cyanosis, coolness, diffuse edema, or perspiration.

- The etiology of RND is unknown.
- Aggressive physical therapy program is needed to regain function. Physical therapy may also include individual or family counseling.

Ronald P. Pfeiffer and Brent C. Mangus
Concepts of Athletic Training FOURTH EDITION

Injury Imitators: Psychologic

When athletes appear to take advantage of secondary gain from their injuries, coaches should remain vigilant for signs of depression.

- A continuum of seemingly minor, yet troublesome injuries should be further questioned.
- Referral to a physician, psychologist, or school counselor is mandatory.

Notes

Ronald P. Pfeiffer and Brent C. Mangus

Concepts of Athletic Training *FOURTH EDITION*

Strength Training

- Many studies have found low rates of injuries among young weight trainers.
- Weight training may help young athletes perform better and be less susceptible to overuse injuries.
- At one time there were concerns that adolescent weight training may be a factor in growth plate injuries, but most of those injuries occurred primarily in unsupervised training programs and the need to lift maximum weights.

16

Ronald P. Pfeiffer and Brent C. Mangus

Concepts of Athletic Training *FOURTH EDITION*

Strength Training (continued)

American Academy of Pediatrics guidelines for weight training:

- Trainees should always be under close supervision.
- Adolescents should reach Tanner stage 5 of sexual maturity before participating in a vigorous weight training program.
- Children should begin a strength training program if they have the interest to do so, are receptive to coaching, and can follow instructions.

17

Ronald P. Pfeiffer and Brent C. Mangus

Concepts of Athletic Training *FOURTH EDITION*

Strength Training (continued)

Safety
- Safety should be the focus of all adolescent weight training programs.
- To avoid injury, young athletes need proper supervision and guidelines.

Eliminate:
  » Single-repetition maximum lifts.
  » Use of Olympic and power-lifting techniques.

18

Notes

_____
_____
_____
_____
_____
_____
_____
_____
_____
_____
_____
_____
_____
_____
_____
_____
_____
_____
_____
_____
_____
_____
_____
_____
_____
_____
_____
_____
_____
_____
_____
_____
_____
_____
_____
_____
_____

Ronald P. Pfeiffer and Brent C. Mangus
Concepts of Athletic Training FOURTH EDITION

Strength Training (continued)

- Safer alternative lifting techniques should be offered.
  - Safer method for assessing an athlete's strength is the following equation:
    - Weight lifted x number of repetitions x 0.03 = 1 RM.
  - Avoid placing body in positions that increase risk of injury.

Ronald P. Pfeiffer and Brent C. Mangus
Concepts of Athletic Training FOURTH EDITION

Prevention of Injury

- **Preparticipation Physical Examination (PPE)**
  - All athletes should have a complete evaluation done by a trained physician prior to entry into organized sports.
- Rehabilitation of Previous Injuries
  - Improperly rehabilitated injuries may increase the risk of re-injury over the next several years and osteoarthritis years after the initial insult.

Ronald P. Pfeiffer and Brent C. Mangus
Concepts of Athletic Training FOURTH EDITION

Prevention of Injury (continued)

- **Stretching** programs lessen injury and improve overall flexibility.
  - Stretching and flexibility exercises should be routine part of conditioning programs.
- **Coaching** techniques – must be knowledgeable in the fundamental techniques of their sport as well as knowing the proper principles of strength and conditioning.
- Special concerns include female athletes with menstrual abnormalities and athletes using prescription stimulant medication.
